KU-789-188

THE HEREFORD & ~~~~~~~~~~
COLLEGE OF NU~~~~ & ~~~WIFERY
WORCESTER CENTRE 887

Contents

NATIONAL INSTITUTE FOR SOCIAL WORK
RESEARCH UNIT

LIBRARY

The Library,
Worcester College of Higher Education,
Henwick Grove, WORCESTER.

Leaving Hospital:

Elderly People and their Discharge to Community Care

The Peirson Library
UNIVERSITY COLLEGE WORCESTER
Henwick Grove, Worcester, WR2 6AJ
Telephone: 01905 855341

Return on or before the last date stamped below.

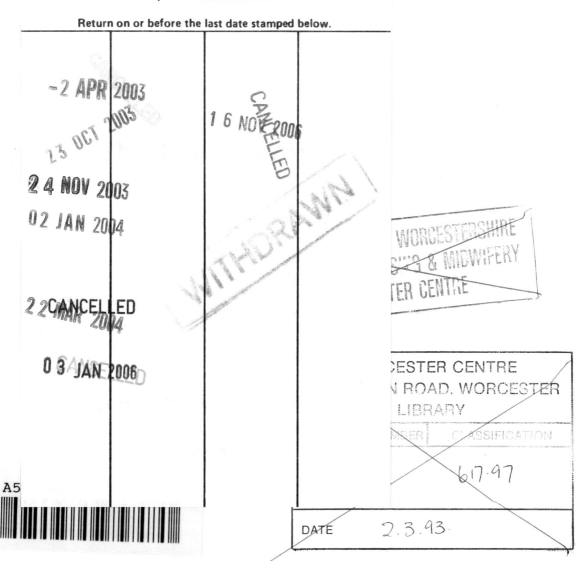

-2 APR 2003

23 OCT 2003

2 4 NOV 2003

02 JAN 2004

1 6 NOV 2006

CANCELLED

WITHDRAWN

2 2 CANCELLED MAR 2004

03 JAN 2006

WORCESTERSHIRE
& MIDWIFERY
TER CENTRE

CESTER CENTRE
N ROAD, WORCESTER
LIBRARY

CLASSIFICATION

617.97

DATE   2.3.93

A5

© Crown copyright 1992
Applications for reproduction should be made to HMSO
First published 1992

ISBN 0 11 701681 0

Further information regarding this and other NISW titles may be obtained from:

National Institute For Social Work
5 Tavistock Place
London
WC1H 9SS

Telephone: 071 387 9681

THE HEREFORD & WORCESTERSHIRE
COLLEGE OF NURSING & MIDWIFERY
WORCESTER CENTRE

Acknowledgements

We are grateful to the Research and Development Division of the Department of Health for financing this research, and for the help of our liaison officers at the Department Sue Moylan, Madeleine Simms and Ruth Chadwick. We much appreciate the support we have received from our Project Advisory Committee.

We also wish to thank our colleagues in the National Institute for Social Work Research Unit. Farzana Majid entered the interview data. Anwar Hussein and Roger Bowater helped with the computing. We appreciate the help received on this report from Dr Jan Pahl. The production of this report has been entirely due to the willingness and word processing skills of Connetta Smith, Kay Thompson, Susy Maclean and Kathy Jowitt.

Throughout the research programme the unit statistician, Peter Gorbach, participated in the planning and process of the project and gave valuable advice on research methods and analysis.

Invaluable and willing help was provided by the Institute's librarian, Giustina Ryan and her team. Julia Phillipson's vitality and skill in acting as a consultant and facilitator for the workshops was reflected in their success.

The people who have participated in this research in four local authorities are too numerous to name. We thank the principal officers who allowed the research to happen. The people who recorded information on hundreds of referrals did so with patience and good humour. These were Eileen Archer, Jolly Burburry, Jean Cooper, Di Hicks, Janet Hodson, Stella Hurtodo and Margaret Smith. We also valued the time and opinions given by the home helps.

We wish to record our particular appreciation of the home help organisers who found time for this work in their busy schedules with so much enthusiasm and humour. Unfortunately, for reasons of confidentiality, we are unable to name them.

The interviewers gave whole-hearted commitment to this work and we are indebted to them for the wealth of information they produced. Interviewers for the telephone survey were Roger Foggitt, Patricia Longbottom, Ann Lusher, Christine North and Mary Ternouth. Interviewers for the feasibility study were Elizabeth Baxter, Margaret Burrows, Vanessa Cahill, Mildred Comber, Anne Cottis, Yvonne Eley, Lucienna Evans, Julie Hickey and Geoff Russell.

Most of all we thank the elderly people and their carers for entrusting us with their opinions and feelings. We hope we can do them justice.

The opinions expressed in this report are those of the authors and not necessarily those of the National Institute for Social Work or of the Department of Health which sponsored the Study.

List of tables

Page

Chapter 1

Background and context of the research

The focus of this report is the discharge from hospital of people aged 75 years or older who were referred for home care in the community.

The demographic, political and economic context of the research

Demographic changes and the projected increase in the numbers of very old people in the population over the next twenty years or so are well documented (Table 1.1). Nationally, at any one time, around 2.5% of elderly people occupy nearly half the hospital beds, while the cost of hospital care per head of those over 75 years old has been around five times greater than for other age groups. Styles of geriatric practice have been shown to influence factors such as bed/population ratio, discharge rates per bed and

Table 1.1 The Elderly Population 1981–2001. Great Britain

	1981	1991	2001	1981–2001 % of change
Total population (thousands) aged:				
65–69	2,667	2,718	2,398	−10.1
70–74	2,265	2,233	2,176	− 3.9
75–79	1,601	1,793	1,825	+14.0
80–84	900	1,208	1,210	+34.4
85+	552	843	1,047	+89.7

Source:

OPCS 1983, table 1; 1989 based projection for the home population mid year as in OPCS 1984, appendix table 1.

consultant/bed ratio. The economic and resource implications of providing hospital care for the very old are therefore obvious and it is essential to ensure that those who no longer require hospitalisation are discharged as quickly and smoothly as possible.

The implementation of the National Health Service and Community Care Act (1990) has initiated basic changes in the organisation of the National Health Service. Urgent attention is increasingly being paid to the need to ensure that resources are used effectively, efficiently and for the purpose for which they are intended. Refined medical skills, heavy demand and long waiting lists for hospital treatments, a sharper definition of the purposes of hospitalisation and reduction in long-stay hospital facilities are all factors which have contributed to shorter inpatient hospital stays and speedier discharge. Yet the process of convalescence or recovery at home may be difficult for those who live alone, especially if they are very old and already frail.

The full implementation of the NHS and Community Care Act will be coupled with the transfer to local authorities of social security payments for residential care. There is an intention in the Act to improve the scope and quality of community care to those who wish to remain in their own homes. This is underpinned by the charters of Citizens' and Patients' Rights which determine the extent to which old people are given rights to influence their community care services or to receive contracts of care when they enter a residential home.

Yet it is difficult to be overly sanguine about the prospects of more extensive community care in the short-term. Demographic change, which has resulted in an increase in the numbers of very old people, also has resulted in a decrease in the proportion of younger elderly people, who may include the caregiving sons and daughters of the very old. Demographic change has also coincided with recession and increased unemployment. The higher ratio of non-wage earners to employed people places greater stress on maintaining existing standards of services.

In 1989 the Department of Health published a document called *Discharge of Patients from Hospital*. This pamphlet contains clear criteria for good practice and procedures in relation to the process of discharge from hospital for people of all ages. It is of crucial importance because it represents the Department of Health's view of the standards to which health and social services should aspire. In particular it states that 'discharge procedures should provide for patients and .... carers to be consulted and informed at every stage and before decisions are made....'.

In 1992 the Department of Health published *The Patient's Charter*. One of the National Charter Standards contained in this relates to the discharge of patients from hospital and states 'before you are discharged from hospital a decision should be made about any continuing health or social care needs you may have. Your hospital will agree arrangements for meeting these needs with agencies such as community nursing services and local authority social services departments before you are discharged. You and, with your agreement, your carers will be consulted and informed at all stages'.

The research background

Humanitarian considerations and the desire for the most appropriate care for very old people are not easy to justify on economic grounds, but form the basis for much professional motivation. Previous research in the Research Unit at the National Institute for Social Work on the characteristics and outcome of applications for statutory residential care under Part III of the National Assistance Act 1948 (Neill *et al.*, 1988) provided evidence of the deteriorated and demoralised state of some who had become patients in long-stay geriatric wards, not because they required on-going medical treatment but because they needed a degree of care which nobody else was prepared or able to give. Insights were also gained into the difficulties which relatively powerless old people might experience in breaking out of the institutional system to return to live in a private household, especially if they had no homes of their own and their relatives were no longer able or willing to give care. In another study in the National Institute for Social Work Research Unit hospitalisation in the year prior to interview was found to be associated with low morale among elderly clients living alone (Sinclair *et al.*, 1988).

Interest and research activity in hospital discharge of elderly people has been continuing for over twenty years and the programme of the Continuing Care Projects (CCP) has been seminal both in pinpointing the issues and in stimulating innovative procedures and practice. From their first publication in 1970 (Skeet, 1970), through some of their subsequent publications (Age Concern, 1975; Amos, 1973; NCCOP 1978 a/b), the CCP have drawn attention to the need for an elderly person's potential difficulty on discharge to be identified early and for adequate services to be provided on the day of their discharge and in the weeks immediately afterwards. These findings have been confirmed and extended by other work and in particular by studies of a large sample of hospital patients discharged in Wales (Victor, nd) and by the sample of patients interviewed in depth in Brighton (Williamson, 1985). Many community health councils have, and are, conducting surveys of patients, including elderly people discharged from hospital. Furthermore, the evaluative studies of the range of innovations in practice will also yield information on sub-groups. Important amongst recent studies is the work conducted at Northwick Park Hospital (Townsend *et al.*, 1988), which evaluated inter-disciplinary assessments on a large sample of elderly people and in a degree of detail which had not been previously available.

Previous studies have consistently shown that hospitalisation is one of the key factors leading to referral to a social services department, especially amongst the elderly. In a community sample in North Wales (Caldock and Wenger, 1988) one half of the people over 60 had been an in-patient since their retirement. The likelihood of hospitalisation and the need for social services following discharge increases with age (OPCS, 1987; Victor and Vetter, 1985). In two North London social services teams (Sinclair *et al.*, 1988) it was found that one fifth of referrals for home help were made by hospitals.

Study of applications for statutory residential care (Part III) showed that hospitalisation of the very old can be an important predeterminate of their subsequent institutional care in either a hospital or residential home (Challis and Davies, 1986; Davies and Challis, 1986; Neill *et al.*, 1988). Greater ease of admission to private and voluntary residential homes for the old since changes in social security payments were implemented in 1980 and the proliferation of such facilities (see Parker, 1990), increased the risk of precipitous and unnecessary admission to permanent residential care following hospitalisation if adequate pre-discharge planning and domiciliary services could not be provided. However, it cannot be assumed that all those who lacked information about various aspects of their care on discharge or who felt unprepared to leave a hospital ward necessarily needed aftercare which they did not have. Skeet (1985) estimated that half the elderly people discharged from hospital nationally needed no aftercare. Other studies varied slightly in the proportions reported. Regardless of the size of the problem, the indications were that there were many elderly people who expressed a need for some type of help on discharge which they did not receive.

Aims of this research

The research described in this report was planned as a feasibility phase for a larger evaluative study. However, the topical nature of the findings and the radical organisational changes outlined above led to a re-appraisal of this programme. The eventual aims were:

1. *To describe approaches to the provision of home help/home care services on discharge in terms of*:
   - the organisation of the home help/home care services;
   - the assessment of clients by home help/home care organisers;
   - the roles and tasks of the home help/home care worker.

2. *To evaluate the effectiveness of various packages of services in terms of*:
   - their perceived relevance to clients and their carers;
   - their impact on particular problems of daily living;
   - their impact on the client's morale and experience of well-being.

As this was a feasibility study it was especially important to use the skill, experience and motivation of participants in order to disseminate the findings and encourage discussion. Therefore a developmental approach was adopted from the beginning and the research programme was interspersed with day and residential workshops.

4

This report

This report contains snapshots in time from different perspectives about the discharge from hospital of very old people who required continuing care in the community from the home help service. These perspectives include:

The national perspective. In 1988/9 a telephone survey was conducted to obtain the views of appropriate principal officers in over 50% of the local authorities in England and Wales about issues relating to hospital discharge. Discussions were also held with two hospital social workers in each authority. (Chapter 2)

The home help service perspective in four local authorities. Referrals to selected home care organisers in four local authorities which were operating different ways of providing home care to old people on discharge were monitored during 1989/90. (Chapters 3 and 4)

The perspectives of old people, their principal carers, their home help organisers and their home helps about individual patients. A sample of 70 people aged 75 years or older was selected from the referrals monitored during 1989/90. All had been referred for home help/home care after a stay in hospital of at least 3 nights' duration. Interviews were held with the above respondents two and twelve weeks after the elderly person's discharge from hospital. (Chapters 5–14)

The perspectives of home help organisers and home helps about their service. Confidential discussions were also held in 1991 with the home help/home care organisers who had participated in the research about the organisational context of their work, their perceptions of the organisational changes which were taking place and their views on their training needs (Neill, forthcoming).

Scope of research

The monitoring and interview studies that we have just outlined formed part of a feasibility study. The constraints of our sample, which include the small sample size, the small number of schemes sampled and the selective eligibility criteria, limit the potential for generalising the findings. The sample was intended to provide a basis for the initial exploration of the impact of services received on discharge from hospital and the effects over time of these. In this feasibility study, it was more important to identify the issues and their possible implications than to estimate the frequency of particular issues or problems. This the study has done.

Chapter 2

National telephone survey of discharge from hospital of frail elderly people

Purpose of survey

This survey, which was conducted in 1988/89, set out to obtain the views of a principal officer and two social workers in over half the local authorities in England and Wales. They were asked about the advantages and shortfalls of current policy and practice in relation to hospital discharge of very old people.

Methods

Selecting the authorities

Fifty seven local authorities were selected at random from the 116 authorities in England and Wales. As it was necessary to do a careful pilot, 21 authorities were also selected from those not in the main study sample. Both main study and pilot samples were structured to represent the 5 types of local authority (inner and outer London boroughs, metropolitan districts, non-metropolitan counties and Wales).

Selecting and interviewing the respondents

The principal officer who was responsible for hospital social work and liaison with hospitals was identified in each authority. One local authority had a divisional structure with three divisional principal officers of equal status. In this one authority all principal officers were interviewed. The principal officers interviewed can be regarded as a random sample of all those in England and Wales.

Four interviewers were appointed who made arrangements with respondents for telephone conversations. Questionnaires were used during interviews. At the end of these interviews each principal officer was asked to nominate two social workers, one who was responsible for discharges from a geriatric ward and another who worked with old people who had been admitted to an acute award via a casualty department. During the sections of the interviews with social workers which concentrated on practice issues, such as procedures for assessment, interdisciplinary collaboration, review and follow up, each social worker was asked to name one ward and to focus their replies on it.

The social workers who were interviewed were not a random sample because they were selected by the principal officers as suitable for the project. As requested, they were experienced in and knowledgeable about the hospital discharge of old people and there is no reason to think they were facing atypical situations in their work. Similar procedures for interviews were followed for both principal officers and social workers.

The response

The research proposal and a letter to the directors of social services resulted in interviews in 51 of the 57 authorities in the main study and 20 of the 21 authorities selected for the pilot. Therefore, views were obtained from principal officers and hospital social workers in 71 local authorities (61% of all authorities in England and Wales). The findings derived from interviews in the 51 main study authorities did not differ in essence from those expressed during interviews in the 20 pilot authorities.

Changes in resources

During the pilot study it was clear that changes, current in 1988, in policy, procedures and resources were already having far-reaching effects on hospital discharge of the very old. Nearly all of those interviewed in the main study emphasised the repercussions for patients and for social services of changes in resources and in the eligibility for hospital care of elderly people.

Cuts in the number of long-stay hospital beds for old people during 1987/88 were reported in two-thirds of the local authorities. Large increases in the numbers of private residential and nursing Home places during the same period were reported in most authorities. No change or a decrease in the number of Part III places were reported by principal officers in four-fifths of the authorities. This was usually because Part III homes were being refurbished to provide private rooms but sometimes because they were being sold. No change or cuts in the 'normal' level of provision of community care services were described by most of those interviewed. Some cuts in provision were masked by changes in criteria for eligibility. For example, three fifths of the principal officers reported that their social services department was considering a change in the rules for eligibility for their home help service. This would exclude people who only required help with domestic tasks and not help with their personal care. One authority had already implemented this change but had reversed it because the repercussions of excluding this group of people from home help were too severe.

Half-way provision

Few respondents said their authority had any adequate residential or day care provision for rehabilitation, convalescence or assessment. This meant that the old people who were still recovering at the time of their discharge from hospital and who required more extensive help than domiciliary services were able to provide, could seldom be held in temporary half way provision until their situation had stabilised. In the opinion of some respondents this could lead to re-admission to hospital, a premature decision for residential care or silent suffering and deterioration in the community.

A small minority of health and social services authorities had developed residential assessment or rehabilitation facilities, sometimes adapting Part III homes for this purpose or designating a hospital ward for rehabilitation.

The implications for practice of changes in resources

Changes in provision

Nearly all principal officers said that there were especially difficult issues in relation to hospital discharge of very old people in their authority.

Changes in provision between health, social service and private sectors had had major repercussions on hospital discharge of old people. The steep decrease in long-stay hospital provision, increase in the private residential sector and a transfer of demand but not of resources to community services meant that hospital discharge of the elderly had become a 'hot' issue. Some principal officers considered change had not happened in a planned, systematic way and was to the detriment of some old people.

Concern was expressed that medical efficiency, influenced by waiting lists, was being measured by swift throughput of patients so that, for example, a patient might be discharged within days of major surgery, irrespective of the age and the state of health of their carer. It was considered that the pressure on old people in hospital to move out, the speed of their discharge, their vulnerable post-illness state, advanced age and lack of information raised ethical issues about their freedom of choice and their need for protection. It has been pointed out that 'whilst the principle of autonomy may be used to support individual choice, it may also be interpreted as encouraging self-reliance, and as a way of denying a collective responsibility to elderly people's care needs' (Chadwick and Russell, 1989).

There was also concern about the 'knock-on' effect of change on Part III care. Several said that the residents of Part III homes were becoming frailer and more 'difficult' as a group because local authorities were accepting those rejected by or transferred from the private sector. Those old people who were too well for the few long-stay hospital beds which remained, yet too frail to be eligible for Part III and had insufficient money to gain access to the private sector, could be returned to inadequate services in the community. Some of these old people might be cared for by relatives of similar age. Principal officers, and some social workers, also said they felt sure that the speedier hospital discharge of very old people had increased their readmission rate, but they had no information to substantiate this impression.

Research findings vary about influences on readmission. Researchers in Wales and in Brighton had found that re-admission to hospital was not a good indicator of the effectiveness of good preparation for hospital discharge or of the adequate and speedy provision of services after discharge. These research studies concluded that re-admission was related more often to the elderly person's age, type of initial disability and current medical condition rather than to other social characteristics. However, both studies also concluded that the patient's expressed feelings about their 'readiness to leave' hospital was a predictor of their subsequent re-admission and they suggested that this aspect of hospital discharge needed further study (Victor, nd; Williamson, 1985). By contrast, other research (Williams and Fitton, 1988) indicates that inadequate preparation for discharge is a factor in subsequent unplanned hospital admission.

Changes in hospital social work

All except seven of the 102 hospital social workers who were interviewed were based solely in a hospital, but a third of these social workers were expecting a change in the way hospital social work was organised in their authority. The development of large district general hospitals meant that the responsibilities of a hospital social work department could span several local authorities, whereas the cost of employing these social workers fell upon the local authority in which the hospital was based. This, together with other changes, such as shorter in-patient stays, was expediting a move to re-organise hospital social work and base these social workers outside hospitals. Nearly all the hospital social workers who were interviewed were apprehensive of the repercussions of such change. However, in only one in four authorities did principal officers report a firm plan for such a change in the foreseeable future. It is worth noting that the only British research study of the location of hospital social work has come down firmly in favour of basing social work in hospitals (Connor and Tibbitt, 1988).

Most principal officers and social workers considered that it was important to retain social workers in hospitals to preserve their ability to respond quickly and to work as members of a multi-disciplinary team. The main disadvantages of a hospital work-base were said to be the risk of becoming isolated from other aspects of social service department work, especially the work in area offices and having divided responsibilities from serving two masters (the NHS and the SSD). The word 'advocate' was frequently used by social workers in relation to their work with very old people; many felt that being the only non NHS employed professional in a NHS setting enabled them to act as a mediator between elderly patients and medical professionals when appropriate.

In most of the British research on hospital discharge of elderly people, however, the role of the hospital social worker does not figure to any great extent. With the exception of patients discharged from geriatric hospitals, only a minority of discharged elderly patients had been referred to a hospital social worker and issues of hospital discharge and aftercare were largely the province of the nursing and medical staff.

Furthermore, the intention of the Seebohm re-organisation to provide a 'continuum of care' between hospital and community did not seem to have made much impact on the aftercare of the old people reported in these studies. Mention was seldom made of area social workers retaining responsibility for the care of elderly people after their admission to hospital nor of hospital social workers continuing to visit elderly people after their discharge home.

In about half of the authorities in which interviews were conducted, principal officers reported that it had not been easy to keep their hospital social workers up to establishment in the past year. One fifth had experienced especial difficulty in recruiting people to fill geriatric social work posts. This was commonly attributed to the lower status and resources accorded to work with elderly people compared to work with children or families. It was also considered to reflect a shortfall in social work training for work with the elderly and the pessimistic attitudes inculcated in relation to work with old people during some social work courses. Over half the hospital social workers said that their team or group had seldom (32%) or never (25%) been fully staffed with social workers during 1987.

Collaboration between professionals

Hospitals and primary health care

Links on discharge between hospital and general practitioners were reported to be weak. Two thirds of the social workers said that, in relation to the ward being considered, general practitioners were not usually informed by the hospital before a discharge had taken place. Furthermore, in only one in three wards were patients routinely given written information about their medication on their discharge. This is particularly significant since most were frail, very old people who might require help from their general practitioner with another medical emergency soon after they arrived home.

There have long been problems over delay in notification from hospitals to general practitioners of the dates of admission and discharge and the types of investigation and medication which had been given to their patients. Research by Young, Wallace and Victor (1991) included a survey of a sample of general practitioners' views of liaison at the interface of hospitals and primary health care. Failure of hospitals to notify general practitioners when their patients were admitted was one of their biggest complaints.

These problems are likely to be increased by the swifter throughput of hospital patients, but solutions through the use of new technology have also received attention. For example, research on the acceptability by 104 general practitioners of four styles of word processor letters (Holyoake and Semple 1990) showed that a short, concise standardised letter was acceptable to most. However, neither of the two preferred styles of letter contained any information about a patient's living group or need for community care services.

Hospital social workers and hospital personnel

In general, the quality of the relationships between social service and hospital personnel in relation to the discharge and care of old people seemed to be a mixture of serious conflict and good collaboration. Whereas half the social workers reported problems in their interdisciplinary relationships, especially with consultants, three quarters also described 'good practices' in interdisciplinary collaboration. Social workers said that current changes had increased pressures on all members of the hospital team and this meant they often had to act as mediators and advocates for elderly patients. This intervention could contribute further to conflict with their medical colleagues.

Four out of five of the hospital social workers who were interviewed had established a system for assessing old people prior to discharge. This reflected the bias in the principal officers' selections of two hospital social workers; they probably selected those who were most interested in work with the elderly. These assessment systems included regular daily meetings with ward or other hospital staff. There was evidence that discharge arrangements worked more smoothly and at a slower pace in geriatric than in other wards. On the geriatric wards selected, nearly all the social workers had planned and regular multidisciplinary discussions about patients, compared with only half those on non-geriatric wards.

There were similar differences in whether these discussions were said to work well. Social workers for geriatric wards more often had access to other assessment facilities, such as a hospital based assessment unit (71% compared with 55%) or a rehabilitation ward (79% compared with 61%). Furthermore, geriatric ward social workers more often reported realistic expectations of their roles by their medical colleagues (57% compared with 32%). Unrealistic expectations mirrored the assumption of doctors that social workers had greater control over obtaining resources quickly than was actually the case. Geriatric ward social workers also more often said they usually had adequate notice of discharge dates to arrange services (71% compared with 37%). If the possibility of making adequate discharge plans in time seemed unlikely, more geriatric ward social workers said their views would usually be listened to (83% compared with 66%). Slightly more also said that the wishes of patients about discharge arrangements would be seriously considered by their medical colleagues (76% compared with 61%).

These results are in line with other research studies, which have found that the quality of discharge procedures and the degree of inter-professional collaboration differed between geriatric and other types of hospital. In geriatric hospitals there was more often discussion with the patient, inter-disciplinary collaboration between medical staff and more careful preparation for discharge. Skeet (1970, 1985) showed that in geriatric hospital wards, physiotherapists and occupational therapists were more often involved in identifying aftercare needs than they were in either acute or in orthopaedic hospital wards.

Social workers in hospitals and area offices

In relation to work with elderly people, liaison between social workers in hospitals and those in area offices was apparently affected by the low priority which had to be given to work with the elderly by area social workers. Half of the hospital social workers described good co-operation with area social workers but the others said that they had limited contact because pressure of work from child abuse and child protection meant that an old person could seldom be taken on as a 'case' in an area office. The main link between hospital social workers and community social services was the home help organiser. Most hospital social workers described good working relationships with organisers, especially where a special hospital discharge scheme had been established.

Health and social service managers

At the management level, two thirds of principal officers said that they were currently experiencing major problems in interdisciplinary relationships, but a half also described 'good practices' in collaboration with their health service colleagues. Conflict between managers over resources or procedures appeared to be more intractable than conflicts between practitioners over individual patients, when some sort of compromise was usually reached. However, managers also had the resources and authority to establish innovative ways of responding to new situations. Foremost amongst these were various types of 'schemes' to facilitate discharge from hospital.

Special hospital discharge schemes

Over half the authorities had set up special 'hospital discharge' schemes which provided elderly people with intensive care for short periods, ranging from a few days to six weeks, after their discharge. These schemes had a variety of names such as 'Home from Hospital', 'Home Care Plus', 'Crisis Team'. Some schemes were available in some parts of an authority but not in others and the ways in which they were financed and staffed also varied. Some schemes involved extending the roles of home helps in mainstream services; others involved establishing separate teams of home care workers. Yet other schemes consisted of a mixture of paid and voluntary workers.

No two schemes were identical, either in the ways they were financed, who managed and staffed them, the groups they served,

Table 2.1 Hospital Discharge Schemes Reported in National Telephone Survey: Number of Schemes, Source of Finance and Type of Local Authority

Source of finance	Type of authority			
	Inner and outer London boroughs	Metropolitan districts	Non-metropolitan counties and Wales	Total no of schemes reported
Existing schemes				
Social services department only	7	6	8	21
Health/social services department	9	4	8	21
Voluntary organisation only	1	1	3	5
Voluntary organisation/ social services department	–	1	1	2
Health department only	–	1	1	2
Health/housing department	–	–	1	1
Health/housing/social services department and EEC	–	–	1	1
Health/housing/social services and Welsh Office	–	–	1	1
Planned schemes				
Social services department	2	2	7	11
Health/social services department	1	–	1	2
Stopped schemes				
Health/social services department	–	1	2	3
No record of finance	2	3	–	5

* There were: 22 London boroughs; 18 metropolitan districts and 31 Welsh and non-metropolitan counties in the sample.

13

the localities they covered or the length of time after discharge during which 'special' help was available to their clientele. Outline information about the ways schemes were financed and the types of local authorities in which schemes were reported is set out in Table 2.1.

Types of local authorities and ways schemes were financed

Forty three of the seventy one local authorities surveyed described some type of special hospital discharge scheme. Five of these authorities reported more than one scheme, which meant that fifty four schemes were described. In addition, eight authorities had had schemes in the past but these had been stopped usually because their finance had run out. Thirteen authorities were planning new schemes at the time of the survey. Three quarters of the London boroughs reported having a scheme as did two thirds of the metropolitan districts and one half of the non-metropolitan counties. Some social service department finance was being provided for over four fifths of the schemes described. Health service finance was being provided to a half of the schemes. In most cases this was through joint health/social service finance budgets.

Although a specific question about volunteers was asked, the work of voluntary organisations in relation to the discharge from hospital of elderly people was almost certainly under-represented in the schemes which were described by principal officers and social workers. There may be various reasons for this lack of information. The bias of the research questionnaire was towards health and social services and not towards the activities of volunteers. Principal officers, who were usually based in central administrative offices, and social workers who were based in hospitals may have been unaware of some of the work of small groups of volunteers in local areas. The activities of volunteers were not always perceived as part of an established system of care. There were some descriptions of volunteer schemes which had ceased because of lack of volunteers, or others which were disregarded because volunteers had been too 'choosy' about the people they would accept for help and about the tasks they were prepared to do. The presence of a voluntary work coordinator in the local authority or hospital was probably an important factor in the coordination and recognition of volunteer effort. Unfortunately, this question was not included in the questionnaire.

'Age' of schemes

Seven of the schemes which were described were established long before more recent changes in health and social service resources. All of these were organised and run by voluntary organisations and showed the influence of the CCP programme which started in the 1970's. The 'oldest' scheme described in this survey started in 1974. In most cases these schemes had defined purposes and limited clientele and goals. For example, one group of volunteers identified all elderly people who were admitted to a hospital casualty department as a result of a fall and visited them at home within one or two days of discharge. Volunteers gave practical help immediately after discharge and referred to statutory agencies for longer-term assistance. Although some respondents described increasing difficulty in recruiting volunteers, the clear and limited aims of some volunteer efforts may have enabled such schemes to survive when others had foundered. Furthermore, it seemed very important for clear aims and functions to be decided and publicised, however limited these were. Such clarity enabled gaps in provision to be identified so that perhaps they might be filled by other volunteers or services.

Types of schemes

The variety of provision through special schemes was very wide. On the one hand, this variety illustrated the range of ways issues around hospital discharge could be tackled and the rich potential which existed for collaborative effort. On the other hand, the ad-hoc development and piecemeal cover of schemes in many authorities illustrated the ways in which service response to a crisis may increase inequity of provision if it is not part of a wider policy plan. Only a minority of schemes were being evaluated systematically and experiences of individual schemes were seldom being shared between local authorities. When the survey was completed four one-day workshops were organised to meet this need for information. These workshops were available to participants in the survey and were over-subscribed.

Schemes which were jointly financed by health and social services more often included medical skills. One in four of these schemes focussed on multi-disciplinary medico-social assessments prior to discharge and in some cases comprehensive assessment programmes had been set up. However, often difficulties were being experienced because the existing health and social service resources in the community were unchanged and were insufficient for some of the assessment recommendations to be implemented after discharge.

Other joint health and social service schemes involved small groups of professionals working together in the community. The memberships of these groups varied and included people such as community psychiatric nurses, occupational therapists, social workers and home help organisers. In most cases these small joint health and social service teams were being piloted in two or three local areas. Other joint schemes were provided only for the patients of one hospital. One scheme had been initiated by one consultant and the intensive care it provided for six weeks after discharge was available only to his patients.

Schemes financed solely by social service departments often involved some sort of development of the home help service. Typically a 'coordinator' or 'organiser' was appointed and was often based in the largest hospital in the authority. Some organisers had teams of home care workers who were able to offer 'intensive' help to patients for varying periods of time after discharge. In one authority this was described as 'emergency short-term help to plug mainstream home help waiting time'. Various reports were received of the effectiveness of such schemes. Some schemes were praised enthusiastically and there were plans to extend them. Others were described as good ideas but were failing because they were too small and too expensive and, in practice, few new patients could be accepted for help. The danger of such schemes becoming silted up, so that there was a waiting list for them, defeated their original purpose of quick response after discharge.

There was an interesting minority of local authorities in which health, social service and voluntary organisations had been linked to provide a more integrated cover of services after discharge. One county authority, for example, had a 'home from hospital' scheme financed by social services, which provided intensive home care for up to six weeks after discharge. A radio controlled night visiting scheme in which a nurse and care assistants could do up to one hundred visits per night had been financed by the health authority. There was also a joint-funded scheme in which two senior nurses had been appointed to liaise with general practitioners and hospitals about the care of the elderly. In addition, a community psychiatric nurse was attached to each social work community team.

In most of the more rural authorities principal officers described logistical problems in getting intensive home care to elderly people. However, villages in rural areas also provided examples of a different type of collaborative effort. In some villages, groups of local residents, sometimes in collaboration with a professional such as a community nurse or social worker, had established a system of providing regular care to elderly ill people or to those who had been discharged from hospital. It was interesting that whereas one village might have an enthusiastic and reliable group of volunteer helpers, other villages nearby completely lacked any sign of communal responsibility. In one or two authorities the social services directorate had given modest financial help to active local groups to show recognition and appreciation of their efforts and to cover their overhead expenses.

More characteristically, however, the hospital discharge schemes revealed by this survey provided intensive care after discharge from hospital for relatively small numbers of people and for limited periods of time. Most schemes appeared to operate against a background of severe pressure on the resources of mainstream home help services.

Where the normal level of home help service provision was low, a crisis could occur at the end of the period of intensive care provided by a 'scheme' for those old people who had not recovered to independent living. Gaps in mainstream resources responsible for continuity of care were cited as problems by 82%

of principal officers and 97% of social workers. Frequently, such gaps in resources were described as minor but vital because they could render the whole system ineffective. For example, over half reported gaps in services at weekends, during the early morning and evening and a similar proportion reported difficulty in obtaining services quickly enough. One authority had a relatively generous provision of mainstream home help services during the day, but had no way of helping an old person into bed at night.

Summary in the context of community care

Overall, the changing role of hospitals, the increased throughput of patients and the growth of private residential provision had presented social service departments with considerable unanticipated demands and challenges at all levels. The need for some elderly frail people to have a period of recovery and special care after their discharge from hospital was emphasised by the principal officers and social workers who were interviewed. However, changes in provision between health and social services meant that intensive care services for old people on their discharge were often patchily provided and seldom able to give comprehensive cover. In no local authority in 1988 was there a fully coherent policy for responding to the new situation in which people were being discharged from hospital quicker and sicker.

Lack of an integrated policy to deal with the knock-on effects of such change on other services had increased conflict between health and social services personnel. Conflict between managers, who were responsible for deploying scarce resources, was said to be more intractable than conflict between practitioners who shared joint responsibility and concern for individual patients.

In the local authorities surveyed there were rarely any day care or residential rehabilitation facilities for those patients who required more structured and intensive programmes for recovery than was possible in their own homes. Inadequate information to patients in hospital and to general practitioners about patients was cited as a general problem in discharge planning. The discharge process was said to include interdisciplinary collaboration more often in geriatric wards than in acute wards.

Half of the local authorities in the sample reported having a hospital discharge scheme. There was wide variety in the ways these schemes were financed, staffed and in their coverage and functions. Some schemes, especially those operated by volunteers, had been in existence for two decades. Other schemes had been set up on a pilot basis and with uncertain finance in response to current difficulties. This meant that a scheme, however successful, might be suddenly discontinued when the finance ran out. Lack of integrated planning could also mean that a securely established and successful discharge scheme had a stressful knock-on effect on the tightly stretched resources of mainstream services.

Nevertheless, respondents described many promising developments. However, there was a need to monitor, evaluate and publicise some of these developments so that the most effective could be identified and replicated and perhaps form the basis for more integrated policy responses.

Chapter 3

Monitoring referrals to home help organisers in four local authorities — methods

In the previous chapter we have described the wide variety of hospital discharge schemes which were reported by a sample of local authorities. Amongst these were schemes which were extensions of a local authority's mainstream home help service and financed solely by the social service department. As described in Chapter One four local authorities in England were selected for the purposes of the research. Each of these authorities had a mainstream home help service and a hospital discharge scheme which was an extension of this. As far as was known, these schemes were securely financed and so were expected to survive at least for the duration of the research.

This chapter outlines the methods involved in monitoring referrals; we shall describe the authorities in which it took place, the four schemes, the methods of collecting information, the type of information sought and obtained and issues arising from the monitoring exercise, especially in relation to the assessment of clients. Our findings based on information at referral will be presented in chapter 4.

Purpose of monitoring

Referrals to hospital discharge schemes and mainstream home help services were monitored for three reasons. Firstly, it was important to identify variations in referrals between the four authorities. Secondly, it was necessary to identify differences in referrals made to hospital discharge schemes and to mainstream services, before further comparisons could be made between the service provided through these two types of provision. Thirdly, information on all referrals would enable the group which was eligible for our research to be identified and used as a sampling frame.

The four local authorities in which the research took place included two London boroughs (B and D) and one division of each of two county authorities (A and C). The social services departments of all four authorities were operating a hospital discharge scheme but, like other local authorities in which schemes had been developed, each of these four schemes had unique features.

Key differences between the authorities are set out in Figure 3.1.

Figure 3.1 Summary of Schemes and Charges for Mainstream Services

	Does the scheme organiser control home help, if so for how long?	Maximum charges per hour and maximum weekly charges* to client for:		Summary description
		scheme	mainstream	
A	Yes For six weeks	No hourly charge £1.50 maximum per week	£2.16 per hour £10.00 maximum per week	Integrated provision: scheme and mainstream helpers may work together.
B	Yes For two weeks	No difference in hourly or weekly charges between scheme and mainstream service. £5.12 per hour No maximum per week		Scheme for 'new' referrals only. Existing home help clients passed to main-stream organisers.
C	No	Not applicable	£3.75 per hour No maximum per week	Assessment and information. All referrals passed to 'patch' organisers.
D	Yes For three weeks	Free	£2.00 per hour £12.00 maximum per week	All referrals of in-patients from several hospitals made to scheme organiser.

* 1990 prices.   Charges relate to clients who are assessed to pay full cost for service.

Authority A

This is a division of a county authority which contains a city surrounded by rural areas.

Hospital discharge scheme

The organiser and her part-time assistant who are responsible for the hospital discharge scheme are based in the large city hospital from which they receive most of their referrals. The organiser is responsible for the work of ten full-time home help assistants. The organiser discusses all potential referrals with ward staff and visits patients in the wards prior to their discharge and often at home after their discharge.

As patients in this district general hospital may come from a large area, the hospital discharge scheme is available to people who live in the city itself and within a ten mile radius of the city boundaries. The service is available to people whether or not they were receiving home help before their hospital admission.

Home help can be supplied from the day of discharge and is available on a seven day a week basis where necessary. A night sitting service is also available. The discharge scheme service is provided for up to six weeks and the clients are then reassessed and referred to mainstream home help organisers if they need continued help. In 1990 there was a maximum charge to clients for the hospital discharge scheme of £1.50 per week. This included the charge for the night sitting service. All the scheme home help workers are casual car users.

Mainstream service

New referrals to mainstream home help services were monitored in two local offices which service a rural area outside the boundary of the hospital discharge scheme. Five mainstream service organisers are responsible for providing home help to an area which contains two market towns, several villages and a scattered farming community.

Co-incidentally, in this area, another type of hospital discharge scheme was being developed during the time of study. The inter-disciplinary relationships which are being developed in this local scheme might have influenced some of the processes of discharge. This scheme was based in the local cottage hospital and was evolved over two years by a multi-disciplinary group which consisted of hospital staff and representatives from the community nursing services and social services. It was decided that the home help and community nursing services would work in collaboration to provide intensive help to patients discharged from the cottage hospital for a maximum period of two weeks after their discharge home. This joint service could be on a daily basis and was provided at a lower cost than the usual mainstream service. The maximum charge in 1990 for the joint service was £1.50 per week. Charges for the mainstream service were £2.16 per hour to a maximum charge of £10.00 per week.

Authority B

This is an outer London borough which is demographically varied. It has a large commercial centre, affluent semi-rural southern boundaries and small older houses and housing estates to the north.

Hospital discharge scheme

The hospital discharge scheme organisers are based in a resource centre for the elderly. Most of their time is spent in two large general hospitals which are situated near to the resource centre. The organiser and her two part-time assistants are responsible for the work of four full-time and three part-time care assistants. This team covers the whole borough and their help is available for up to two weeks after discharge.

People requiring home help on discharge from hospital are referred to the discharge scheme workers *if they did not have a home help before their hospital admission.* If they were already receiving home help before hospital admission they are referred directly to the mainstream organiser in their local district office on their discharge.

The organisers discuss patients with ward staff before discharge and visit patients on the ward. Home help can be provided from the day of discharge and is available on a seven day per week basis if necessary. Charges in 1990 for the hospital discharge service and for the mainstream service were the same and between £1.28—£5.12 per hour. All schemes home help workers are supplied with bleeps and are casual car users.

Mainstream service

Referrals were monitored to one division of the mainstream home help service. This division is one of six in the borough and covers the locality in which the hospital discharge scheme is based. Four organisers manage the home help service in a locality which contains small older housing, some of which is in a poor state of repair.

Authority C

This is a division of a county authority which covers a coastal strip and contains a large town and several coastal resorts. Inland there are villages and rural areas.

Hospital discharge scheme

The hospital discharge scheme organiser is based in a hospital adjacent to the large acute hospital in which she spends most of her time. Most of her referrals are received from the large acute hospital and nearby ophthalmic hospital. This organiser works alone, with a part-time clerical assistant, *and does not have a team of home help workers responsible to her.* She has a large and increasing number of referrals.

This organiser's role is mainly liaising, negotiating and educating. She assesses patients prior to discharge while they are on the ward, discusses referrals with ward staff and provides a range of information to staff and patients about private and voluntary sources of health as well as statutory provision.

Around one third of the referrals to the schemes organiser are referred to the 'patch' locality in which the patient lives for mainstream home help service. As each 'patch' is autonomous and may have somewhat different criteria for eligibility for service, such variations require interpretation to the patients and medical staff. The organiser is also responsible for communicating the patient's needs to the patch concerned. She cannot guarantee that the service she recommends will be provided by the patch home help organiser.

Mainstream service

Referrals to the mainstream home help service were monitored in one patch office in the same large coastal town in which the hospital discharge scheme was based. Five organisers are responsible for providing service to people in a hilly older area of the town which contains local authority flats in tower blocks, a sheltered housing complex for the elderly, but which has no resource centre or Part III home. Age Concern volunteers provide a free volunteer service to patients for two weeks after their discharge. The charge for mainstream home help in 1990 was £3.75 per hour.

Authority D

This is an inner London borough which contains similar demographic variety as Authority B. The hospital discharge scheme full-time organiser is responsible for ten home helps (eight full-time equivalents). The team is based in offices attached to a district social services office in the centre of the borough.

All residents in the borough who require home help on discharge from hospital are referred to the hospital discharge scheme organiser, which means that she receives a large number of referrals from at least fifteen hospitals which serve the borough on a regular basis. This organiser assesses all referrals on written or telephone information supplied to her, and decides whether a further assessment is required. This is done either by herself or her home help workers. On average, the organiser does a further assessment by interview on around a quarter of the referrals made to the scheme.

About three quarters of these referrals are passed directly to the mainstream home help organisers who work in six district offices in the borough.

If a case is selected for help by the hospital discharge team, a home help can be provided from the day of discharge for up to three weeks. Help can be provided daily for seven days per week if necessary and is free to clients. All the hospital discharge schemes home help workers are supplied with bleeps and are casual car users.

This organiser had three roles: to filter referrals, to provide some people with help from her own team, and to refer others on to the mainstream home help services in the authority. The organiser of this scheme, like the organiser of scheme C, had no guarantee that her recommendations would be put into effect by patch organisers who provided mainstream services.

Mainstream service

As all people on discharge from hospital and needing home help are referred to the hospital discharge scheme, no referrals to mainstream services were monitored in this local authority. However, a sample of people who were referred to the mainstream service via the hospital discharge scheme were interviewed. The charges for the mainstream service in 1990 ranged from £2.00 per hour to a maximum of £12.00 per week.

Overview of schemes and their relationships with mainstream services

Schemes

Schemes A and B are similar in that the organisers are in close daily contact with the hospital staff in one or two large hospitals from where most of their referrals originate. In both authorities, the organisers have responsibility for a team of nine home help workers all of whom have cars. The schemes' home help workers work as a team and have regular meetings, together and individually, with the organisers.

In both authorities A and B there is a good deal of 'give and take' between schemes' organisers and the organisers who provide the mainstream home help services. This eases the process of transition between schemes and mainstream provision for both the client and the service providers. In authority A, home help on discharge is sometimes provided by schemes and mainstream workers who work in tandem with a client, sharing the need to cover different parts of the day or week.

There is a strong impression that the senior organisers of both these schemes are well known and respected by the hospital staff with whom they work and that their perspective on the advisability of discharge is taken into account during the decision process.

Scheme D is similar to schemes A and B in that the organiser also has a team of home helps who can provide clients with a period of intense service. Therefore in schemes A, B and D the organisers can provide a service which is based on their own assessment.

However, the organiser in scheme D does not have the degree of personal contact with hospital staff which is possible in schemes A and B. Because her referrals come from a large number of hospitals, this organiser has to filter those which she will assess personally from those which she will pass to mainstream organisers for assessment and service provision.

The considerable experience of this organiser and the length of time she has been in post means that she knows and is known in the hospitals involved, and can make authoritative requests to hospitals for full information on which to base her decisions. This arrangement has a potential for causing stressful relationships between the schemes organiser and mainstream organisers.

Scheme C is a hospital discharge scheme which *separates the assessment role from the provision of service*. The work of this organiser influences a high standard of multi-disciplinary assessment of patients in hospitals prior to their discharge. Patients to be discharged are also given a range of information which enables them to choose a package of integrated care from statutory and voluntary provision. However, the scheme organiser has no guarantee that her recommendations will be put into effect by patch organisers who provide mainstream services.

Although giving autonomy to patches over eligibility for services might facilitate responses to local need, variations between patches in their criteria for eligibility and priority, stress on mainstream resources and different policies about whether or not 'domestic only help' can be provided result in difficulties. These are especially evident when there is need to interpret an authority-wide service to staff of large hospitals.

From the view-point of staff in large hospitals, it may be almost impossible to encompass the variety in criteria for eligibility and priority operated by different autonomous patches within one local authority social services department. Such difficulties may be compounded by non-coterminous boundaries. Thus, one social services department, with or without patches, may have to deal with more than one health district. Similarly, a hospital, especially a large district general hospital, may have to deal with several social services departments and their patches.

Mainstream home help services

In each of these four local authorities a group of mainstream home help organisers were also selected. Referrals to these organisers were monitored during the same period as referrals to schemes organisers were being monitored. This enabled some comparisons to be made between the incoming workload of schemes and of parts of the mainstream home help services in the same authority.

However, like hospital discharge schemes, mainstream services also differed in their context and staffing. In the two London authorities (B and D) the mainstream organisers provided a service to areas which contained pockets of older housing, some of which was in a poor state of repair. There were also areas of apparent affluence in which, in the words of one organiser 'you could find old people rattling around in large houses which they could no longer afford to repair or to keep heated'. By contrast, in one (A) of the two county authorities mainstream home help services were monitored in a very rural area which contained small villages. Interestingly, some villages had developed comprehensive community care services, using volunteers from within their own community. Other villages had no local care networks and home helps had to travel long distances to give care to people who lived in isolated hamlets.

In the two county authorities (A and C), referrals were also monitored to organisers who were responsible for services to seaside resorts. These mainstream services had difficulty over recruiting home helps because of competition from the local hotels who could offer prospective home helps higher rates of pay and more predictable conditions of service.

The types of variation outlined above influences the comparisons which can be made between referrals to different organisers. However, any similarities between referrals, despite the differences in the contexts in which they were made, raises questions about how the home help service is, in general, perceived by referrers.

The similarities between the three schemes (A, B and D) which included a team of home care workers allows comparison between the impact on patients and their carers of a specially organised intensive period of care and the impact of mainstream home help services which often had to be spread more thinly over a longer period of time.

The fourth hospital discharge scheme (scheme C) was of particular interest because the organiser's role was to assess but not to provide a service. As already mentioned, this separation of assessment from provision of service is similar to the assessment/care manager model which may arise from implementation of the NHS and Community Care Act.

Monitoring

All referrals to the four schemes described above were monitored. In addition, all referrals to the selected mainstream home help organisers were also monitored in authorities A B and C. Referrals to mainstream organisers in the fourth authority were not monitored because all people needing home help following discharge from hospital were filtered through the scheme. Monitoring took place over varying periods of time during 1989–1990, but comprehensive monitoring in all four authorities started on 1st February 1990.

Staffing

It was essential for the monitoring of referrals and the subsequent interviews to be done in a similar way in all four authorities. Reliable monitoring of referrals in offices with unique systems was possible only because we were able to obtain the overtime services of clerks who were either working with the organisers or who had done so in the past. These clerks were experienced people who understood the recording systems, knew where files were kept and when it was convenient to ask organisers for information. In two 'patch' offices in rural areas, clerks could not be identified and so monitoring was done by an organiser.

Definition of 'referral'

Referrals to mainstream services may be defined differently from referrals to hospital discharge schemes. A person who has a home help before admission to hospital may not be defined as a 'referral' on their discharge from hospital back to a mainstream home help service, but is likely to be regarded as an existing case where there has been a gap in provision. New systems were developed to cope with the variations in the definitions used by service providers.

Information obtained about referrals

Information on each referral was recorded on a card, designed for the purposes of the research, by clerks who were familiar with the office in which monitoring was taking place. The monitoring card was in three sections.

Section One sought information on the social characteristics of the person being referred, such as their age, gender, ethnicity and household size. It also sought basic information about the referral, such as the date of referral, how and by whom the referral was made and who took the referral information. Where the prospective client was resident on the date of referral and whether they had been in hospital prior to referral was also recorded, as was the date of discharge from hospital and the reason for referral to the home help service.

Section Two was to be completed after the organisers' assessment visits and sought information about the conclusions of their assessments. Pre-coded questions asked whether home help was needed and was to be provided and the number of hours and days it was anticipated home help would be required. If home help was not to be provided there was a small space for the reason to be entered. This was not always completed.

Sections One and Two of the monitoring card enabled the referrals which were eligible for our further research to be selected. The three criteria for eligibility we used were that the person referred should be:

- aged 75 years or older;
- referred following a hospital admission of at least 3 nights duration;
- provided with home help.

In general there was a satisfactory response to questions in Sections One and Two of the card.

Information about assessment which was sought but not obtained

The monitoring card contained a third section which contained pre-coded questions about the client's physical condition and mental state, whether they had relatives or friends who were involved in their care and what other services were to be provided.

It was anticipated that the organiser would obtain this information during her assessment of the referred client and that this part of the monitoring card could be completed. This assumption was mistaken. Section Three was completed on a regular basis in only one authority, and that was by a hospital discharge scheme organiser.

Issues arising from monitoring

Job titles

In each of the four authorities home help 'organisers' had different job titles, for example, Home Care Managers, Community Care Organisers, Resource Officers. For the purposes of this report managers of mainstream home help services and of hospital discharge schemes are all called 'organisers'. Furthermore, all home helps and home care workers are called 'home helps'.

Assessment and missing information

Various reasons were given for the fact that organisers did not possess, at referral, the information sought on Section Three of the monitoring card. Short notice of discharge necessitated brief assessments before discharge, which were later extended by further assessment after the patient had arrived home. It was said that ability to walk or to rise from a chair unaided and to perform other self-care tasks could not be assessed in a ward when the patient was either sitting in a chair or was in bed. Most importantly, organisers considered that whereas the need for service could be assessed before discharge, the precise tasks for which help was required could only be identified in the context of the patient's own home. This meant that, ideally, assessment in two environments, the ward and the patient's own home, was necessary.

However, the more common reason for the non-completion of Section Three of the card was revealed during informal discussions with organisers. It was apparent that organisers who had a heavy volume of referrals, very short notice of referral and were required to provide a service quickly were sometimes unable to see the referred person themselves before home help was provided. This meant that it was home helps rather then organisers who were responsible for assessing need. This assessment was done after discharge when the home help first called on the client. Usually this assessment was followed by a visit from the organiser if the client had not had a home help prior to hospitalisation. It seems that people who had a home help before their admission and who resumed contact with the same home help after discharge might not be personally reviewed by the organiser unless the home help requested this.

As well as variations in whether assessment was done by the organiser personally, there was also variation in how it was done. A few of the assessments in mainstream services consisted of very brief visits. Assessments by hospital discharge schemes were usually more comprehensive. Typically, the hospital discharge schemes organisers who were in close touch with hospital personnel in authorities A and B met referred patients in the ward and sometimes also visited them at home.

The hospital discharge scheme organiser in authority C was very experienced and required a high standard of comprehensive information from referrers. This organiser did very careful assessments on patients who were referred to her and fostered much interdisciplinary liaison within the hospital. The problems faced by this organiser were that she neither had her own team of workers who could carry out her recommendations nor did she always encounter interest from her colleagues in the many patch offices in her local authority. The inequity of provision between patches was difficult for her to explain convincingly to professional colleagues or to patients. This organiser almost certainly gave many patients considerable help and support through the process of discharge from hospital and she also provided them with as much information as possible about alternative sources of help after their discharge. The lack of status accorded to her role meant that her assessments might not be applied to service provision and the interprofessional links she forged within the hospital might not be extended to community service providers. Most importantly, reassurance could not honestly be given to patients about the extent, quality and speed of care they would receive after they had been discharged home.

This research suggests that the role of home helps in assessment is crucial. To some extent, this role is inevitable whether or not the organiser is also personally involved in the assessment process. It may be impossible to forecast how an elderly person will react to their recent illness and to the practical challenges of daily living until they are at home. Home helps who visit during these early days are inevitably key people in this initial process of adaptation, assessment and review. Whereas some home helps seemed skilled, experienced and interested in this role, others were not. The need for a structure for assessment, training in the skills required and a recognised status for home helps who do this are indicated.

Summary in the context of community care

This chapter describes the ways referrals for home help were monitored in a part of four local authorities, each of which had a hospital discharge scheme. The characteristics of these schemes and of the mainstream home help services and the difficulties over obtaining information are described.

It was found that:

- 'a referral' was defined differently by hospital discharge schemes and mainstream services;

- charges to clients varied between local authorities and between schemes and mainstream services in the same authority;

- information about patients' mobility, self care abilities and care networks was generally not obtained before discharge by ward staff and by organisers.

The hospital discharge schemes studied illustrated three types of relationship of assessment to service provision.

Integrated. In schemes A and B organisers worked with one or two hospitals and implemented their assessment conclusions through their own team of home helps.

Separated. In scheme C the organiser had no team of home helps; her role was solely assessment and referral on to mainstream services.

Combined. In Scheme D the organiser filtered all discharges where home help was requested, from at least fifteen hospitals. Some patients were helped by her own team of home helps, others were referred to mainstream services.

In both schemes and mainstream services it was reported that the roles of organisers and home helps in continuing assessment in the home environment were crucial.

Chapter 4

Monitoring referrals to home help organisers in four local authorities — findings

Numbers of referrals

The monitoring involved all the people of all ages who were referred from any source to the four schemes organisers and to their mainstream counterparts. A total of 2035 referrals gathered between January and August 1990 were analysed, as shown in Table 4.1.

Table 4.1 Numbers of Referrals to Home Help Service Monitored in Four Local Authorities

Referral	Department									
	A (322)		B (253)		C* (618)		D* (842)		Total (2035)	
	N	%	N	%	N	%	N	%	N	%
Hospital discharge scheme	152	47	148	58	437	71	842	100	1579	78
Mainstream service	170	53	105	42	181	29	–	–	456	22

* See text for description of the way referrals were received and passed on to mainstream services.

As can also be seen in Table 4.1 a similar number of referrals were monitored from the hospital discharge schemes and mainstream services in authorities A and B and from the mainstream service in authority C. The scheme organiser in authority C was assessing nearly three times as many referrals as her counterparts in authorities A and B, but had no responsibility for a team of home helps. No referrals to mainstream services were monitored in authority D. This was because all referrals of people who required home help on their discharge from hospital were made to this organiser and not to mainstream services directly. The large volume of referrals to this scheme was influenced by the large number of hospitals which served the population of authority D. These special situations in authorities C and D meant that 78% of the 2035 referrals which were monitored were made to a hospital discharge scheme. Referrals to the scheme in authority D accounted for a half of these.

**Table 4.2
Department/
Referral to
Hospital Discharge
Scheme/
Mainstream
Service and Rate of
Referral for Period
February-April
1990**

	All referrals (1309)	Average no. referrals per month for period (1309)	Range per month for period
	%	N	N
Dept A			
HD*	8	33.7	24–40
MS	11	48.0	35–59
Dept B			
HD	11	46.3	45–48
MS	7	31.7	25–37
Dept C			
HD	18	77.7	72–82
MS	6	26.0	24–27
Dept D			
HD	40	173.0	160–194

* HD: Hospital Discharge Scheme
 MS: Mainstream Service

Rates of referrals

The overall periods during which referrals were monitored did not coincide precisely in all four authorities. In order to compare referral rates, a common period of three months between February and April 1990 was selected. Lack of clarity about how effectively the research system for standardising definitions of referral operated, means that these rates should be treated with caution.

As can be seen from Table 4.2, the average number of referrals per month to the hospital discharge scheme in local authority department D was between two and five times greater than the number of referrals to the other three schemes. Even this number of referrals did not always include existing mainstream home help clients who were briefly admitted to hospital. If discharge from hospital of those who require continuing community care is to be regarded as a situation which requires special attention, the numbers of referrals coming to this organiser indicates the size of the potential demand.

The referral rate to scheme B was higher than to scheme A, although scheme B only accepted referrals of people in hospital who had not had a home help prior to the admission. Therefore, it might be expected that the rate of referrals to scheme B would be lower than to scheme A. The range per month of referrals to scheme A was much broader than to scheme B but the reasons for this are unclear. The teams of home helps in the schemes in authorities A and B were both working to their maximum capacities.

The number of hospital beds being covered were similar in authorities A, B and C. Yet the scheme organiser in authority C was receiving considerably more referrals. The reasons for this variation are unclear. As the scheme organiser in authority C was not responsible for providing help from her own team to the people she assessed she may have been more open to demand and more pro-active in encouraging ward staff to detect need for home care after discharge. If such dynamics are in operation they have important implications for the repercussions on demand of the separation of assessment from service provision which may result from implementation of the NHS and Community Care Act.

Formal referral date and notice of discharge

The formal date of referral which was recorded by the clerks in both the mainstream and hospital discharge offices was not necessarily the date on which informal discussion took place between the schemes' organisers and ward staff.

Somewhat surprisingly, the length of formal notice of discharge overall was similar for mainstream and schemes organisers. Only 8% of referrals were made before the patient was discharged home. One fifth (18%) were received on the day of discharge. Over half (56%) of all referrals were received during the week following the client's discharge from hospital. A further 18% were referred even later than the week following discharge.

There were, however, variations both between authorities and between hospital discharge schemes in this respect. Organisers in schemes in authorities A, B and C received longer notice of discharge, which probably reflected their regular daily contact with ward staff. By contrast, in local authority D, the organiser was unable to be in regular personal contact with staff in the many hospitals referring people to her and she seldom received referrals before the day on which the patient was to be discharged. Most (94%) of her referrals were received either on the day of discharge (10%) or after it had happened (84%).

In the mainstream services, most referrals from hospitals were made either on the day of discharge or after it had happened. Interestingly, the highest proportion (22%) of pre-discharge referrals in the four mainstream services were made to the organisers who served the very rural area in authority A. It is possible that hospital personnel recognised the particular difficulties of providing services quickly in this area. By contrast, only 10% of referrals from hospitals to the mainstream organisers in London authority B were before the day on which the patient was being discharged home, 45% were made on the day of discharge and the rest of the referrals were received after the patient had arrived home.

This situation caused distress to the elderly people and to the organisers who were concerned about elderly people being discharged home without services. It also exacerbated poor relationships between organisers and hospital personnel. As one organiser said: *'They (the hospital staff) don't seem to think the home help service requires planning. I think they think we keep home helps in a cupboard, ready to take out at a moment's notice'.*

Who took the referral?

Information on around half of all referrals was first taken by home help organisers or their assistant organisers. On one third of the referrals information was taken by the home help clerk, other clerical or administrative staff or by other people, such as duty social workers.

Because referrals were often received at very short notice, the quality of information obtained from the referrer was important. The researcher was told that when an organiser had a home help clerk who received referrals, more appropriate and fuller information was obtained. Informal observation of records supported this opinion. During the pilot phase of the research the researcher read many inadequate records of referrals received via duty social workers or centrally based clerical staff. The impression was gained that home help clerks became specialised in receiving referrals and obtained more comprehensive information which facilitated quick and appropriate provision of service.

Characteristics of patients referred

Age

Two thirds of the 2035 people referred to hospital discharge schemes and mainstream home help services were aged 75 years or older, including a quarter who were 85 years or older. People referred in authority D were older (average age 78.5 years) than the rest of the sample. As referrals in authority D comprise two fifths of all referrals monitored, they influence the average age of the sample as a whole.

Details of age, gender and household composition are set out in Table 4.3. It was interesting to find that referrals to the hospital discharge schemes, and especially to the scheme in authority A, contained proportionately more people under the age of 60 years.

The organisers in the hospital discharge schemes in both departments A and B were in regular consultation with hospital staff, and so it is not surprising that a broader spectrum of referrals of people of all ages were made to them. In part, this reflects the more flexible roles of hospital discharge home help workers. The post-operative recovery of mothers who had young children at home, and the continuing care of terminally ill people of any age, were some of the situations referred to these hospital discharge schemes. Hospital discharge schemes which became

Table 4.3
Selected Characteristics and Referral to Hospital Discharge Scheme/Mainstream Service

	Dept A		Dept B		Dept C		Dept D	Depts A B C	
	HD (152)	MS (170)	HD (148)	MS (105)	HD (437)	MS (181)	all refs (842)	HD (737)	MS (456)
Age group	%	%	%	%	%	%	%	%	%
0–59	17	5	14	6	5	15	5	6	6
60–74	24	18	32	27	29	20	20	32	25
75–84	36	53	37	41	46	48	45	42	48
85+	23	24	17	25	19	17	30	20	21
Average Age (yrs)	71.2	77.9	72.3	77.3	76.5	73.5	78.5	74.5	76.0
Gender									
male	27	30	25	25	33	25	25	30	27
female	73	70	75	75	67	75	75	70	73
Household composition									
alone	63	70	61	64	67	70	82	65	68
with 1 other	26	24	27	34	30	24	18	28	26
with 2+ others	11	5	12	2	4	7	1	7	5

HD—Hospital Discharge Scheme   MS—Mainstream Service
Percentages exclude missing records which total 3% for age; 1% for gender, and 4% for household composition. Sub totals may not add to 100% because of rounding percentages.

well-known and popular with hospital personnel could become the victims of their own success, if resources were not available for them to expand to meet such increasing and varied demand.

Gender

Overall, women outnumbered men by 3 to 1 among those who were referred to each group of organisers except for referrals to the hospital discharge scheme in local authority C. Here the ratio of women to men was 2 to 1. The reasons for this difference are not immediately apparent. Furthermore, in relation to all referrals, men were under-represented in the referrals of younger clients. Of the small group of 52 people referred who were under 40 years old, only 13% were men compared with 27% of all referrals of all ages. There may be several interesting reasons for this difference, including the needs of sick mothers with young children, maternity cases, and differences in morbidity between the genders in the younger age groups. Expectations about the caring roles of men and women may vary, so that it is considered appropriate for female relatives rather than formal services to care for men who have been in hospital, whereas there may be less expectation for men to give unassisted nursing care to their female relatives.

Household composition at usual residence

Overall, 72% of referrals were of clients who lived alone and Table 4.3 shows that there was little difference between mainstream and scheme referrals in this respect. However four fifths of the people referred to the scheme in authority D usually lived alone.

Table 4.4 presents a profile of the social characteristics of the people who were referred and monitored during the research and compares these characteristics with their ages. Throughout this table the influences of the large group of people referred to the discharge schemes in authorities D and C who were also older (average ages 78.5 years and 76.5 years respectively) must be kept in mind.

Table 4.4
Selected
Characteristics of
All Referrals and
Age Group of
Client

	Age Group (yrs)				Total
	0–59 (148)	60–74 (463)	75–84 (872)	85+ (483)	(2035)*
	%	%	%	%	%
Referral to department:					
A	22	13	14	14	15
B	18	16	11	10	12
C	33	35	32	23	31
D	27	36	42	52	42
Client's gender:					
male	22	35	27	22	27
female	78	65	73	78	73
Household composition:					
alone	33	65	73	81	70
with 1 other	28	30	22	16	23
with 2+ others	36	2	1	1	4
(no record)	3	3	3	2	3
Residence at date referral:					
hospital	69	79	77	81	78
own home	28	18	20	15	19
reln/friend's home	1	0	0	1	0
other	1	1	0	–	0
(no record)	2	2	3	3	3
Client was in/had been in hospital at referral:	81	87	82	84	83

* This total includes missing records for age in 69 cases (3%) which have been excluded from percentages.
Missing records for characteristics have not been excluded from percentages.
Sub totals may not add to 100% because of rounding percentages.

Table 4.4 (*continued*)

	Age Group (yrs)				Total
	0–59 (148)	60–74 (463)	75–84 (872)	85+ (484)	(2035)*
	%	%	%	%	%
Referral from:					
ward sister/nurse	19	31	26	22	25
hosp social worker	45	38	39	46	41
area social worker	7	2	1	1	1
other SSD	9	12	14	16	14
other health	13	8	9	5	8
other	6	7	10	8	8
(no record)	1	1	2	2	2
Referral taken by:					
HHO/Asst HHO	43	53	48	44	48
duty social worker	5	4	4	4	4
other social worker	1	1	1	1	1
HH clerical/admin	27	33	37	42	36
other clerical/admin	22	7	8	9	9
other	1	1	0	0	1
(no record)	1	1	1	1	1
Method of referral:					
telephone	74	67	72	77	72
letter	13	26	22	18	21
personal discussion	10	6	5	3	5
(no record)	2	1	1	1	1
Is home help needed?					
yes	63	53	51	48	50
no	12	12	11	7	10
(no record)	25	35	38	45	40
Is home help to be provided/ recommended?					
yes	43	28	29	30	31
no	10	4	3	3	4
not applicable					
—not needed	12	12	11	7	11
—can't provide	13	23	19	15	18
(no record)	22	33	38	44	37

The size of household varied according to the age of the person being referred. Two thirds of those referred who were under 60 years old lived in households containing other people and only one third were living alone. By comparison, as Table 4.4 shows, four fifths of the people who were aged 85 years or older were living alone.

Other studies have shown that home helps are very much more likely to be provided to people who live alone (Caldock and Wenger, 1988; Hunt, 1978; OPCS, 1987). Disproportionately fewer elderly people who live with others are referred. This may reflect social attitudes towards carers in a situation of limited resources. On occasions, people have been regarded as ineligible for services simply because there are fit people in the same household.

Residence at referral

For obvious reasons most of those people who were referred to hospital discharge schemes were still in hospital when the application was made. However, Table 4.6 shows that one in three referrals to mainstream organisers were also of people who were currently or had recently been in hospital.

Ethnicity

In local authority B it was not accepted policy to record ethnicity. In the other three authorities only 25 (1%) of the 1,782 people who were referred and monitored were recorded as being black (11), Asian (9) or 'other' (5). Nearly all (95%) of people referred in these three authorities were recorded as white and in 4% ethnicity was not recorded. The reasons for this disproportionately low number of referrals of people from black and minority ethnic groups to both hospital discharge and mainstream home help services clearly requires further investigation (Gorbach, forthcoming). Other research studies indicate under-representation of minority ethnic groups in social services for elderly people (Butt *et al.*, 1991; Williams, 1990).

Referrals from hospital social workers

The main source of referrals to organisers were hospital social workers who made 41% of the referrals which were monitored. To identify the possible impact of hospital social work on the discharge process the sixteen hundred and sixty one elderly people who had been in hospital prior to their referrals were selected. Nearly half (48%) of these had been referred by hospital social workers, but there was considerable variation between authorities. Two thirds of the referrals to organisers in authorities B and D had been made by hospital social workers compared with a quarter of the referrals in authority A and 8% of the referrals in authority C.

No other differences in referrals made by hospital social workers could be identified. The people they referred had similar social characteristics of age, gender and living groups. Hospital social workers did not give organisers longer notice of discharge nor did they apparently make a higher proportion of appropriate referrals.

The need for home help

On all referrals organisers were asked to record whether they thought the person being referred needed a home help and to record whether a home help was to be provided or recommended. There was no clear reply to the question of need for two fifths of the referrals. However, one half were recorded as needing and the remaining tenth as not needing a home help.

Half of the people aged 85 years or older were recorded as 'needing' a home help compared with nearly two thirds of those under 60 years of age. Definite plans to provide a home help were recorded in around one in three of the people who had been referred for this service. However there was a very high proportion (39%) of 'no records' to this question which, in part, reflected some organisers' reluctance to commit themselves until further assessments had been made.

There were great variations between authorities and schemes in response to this question of need. In authority D the organiser selected one fifth of the referrals she received for help from her team and passed four fifths on to mainstream services for their assessment and decision about need. By contrast, in authority A, most (96%) referrals to the hospital discharge scheme organiser were considered by her to require home help from her own team of home help workers. In authority C the hospital discharge scheme organiser was not responsible for providing any service and had no team of home help workers. Although she considered that 84% of people referred to her needed home help, she could only recommend this to the mainstream organisers.

Stated need for home help was not related to the household composition or gender of the people referred, neither was it related to whether or not they were in hospital when the referral was made. However, stated need for home help appeared to be related to the discharge process. If referrals were taken by home help organisers or assistant organisers themselves, rather than by clerical or administrative staff or duty social workers, the elderly person was more likely to be regarded subsequently as needing home help service. Referrals made by ward sisters or nurses, and referrals made in writing rather than by telephone, were more likely to be regarded as needing the service.

There were also interesting variations in relation to 'need' between discharge schemes and mainstream services in the same authority. For example, in authority A the scheme organiser considered that 96% of the referrals she received 'needed' the service but this view was stated on only 60% of referrals made to mainstream services in the same authority. Similarly, whereas the organiser in authority C considered that 84% of the people referred to her needed home help, only 48% of referrals received by mainstream organisers in authority C were considered to need this service.

There may be several reasons for these differences. Better liaison between schemes organisers and key staff on the hospital wards meant that more people were being given better information and more realistic expectations of home help services. The high number of apparently inappropriate referrals to mainstream home help organisers meant frustration for the person being referred and wasted time for their carers and home help organisers. In a very few cases it reflected a request for meals on wheels and thus organisational differences in definitions of a 'referral'.

During informal conversation with the researcher, organisers who provided mainstream services said that they felt that home help was still a service which some referrers offered automatically and with little awareness of the roles of home helps. On occasion, referrers did not find out whether home help was a service which the person either sought, needed or wanted. Clearer information to referrers and to the general population about the roles and constraints of the home help service, a sharper understanding of the type and quality of information required at referral, and information about the costs of the service to users and the means testing involved were thought by organisers to be important conditions for reducing the number of inappropriate referrals to them. A more secure and precise status of the home help organiser would undoubtedly improve the process of referral, of assessment and therefore of service delivery because it might increase the confidence of organisers to identify and require acceptable standards of referral to them.

Provision of home help service

There were significant gaps between concluding that a service was needed and planning to provide it. In all four authorities it was policy to accord lower priority to people who required help only with domestic tasks. On all the referrals which were monitored, organisers planned to provide home help to one third of the people referred, but there was variation between authorities. In authorities A and B if either hospital discharge schemes or mainstream organisers decided the client needed a service this service was usually provided. By contrast, in authority C, the hospital discharge organiser did not know whether her recommendation to the mainstream organisers for the provision of service would be accepted. Autonomous patches meant that different criteria for eligibility and priority could be in operation. This resulted in inequality of provision according to where people lived. In authority D the organiser was filtering a large number of referrals of people discharged from hospital and potentially requiring home help. The organiser of this scheme referred on four fifths of her referrals but she did not know whether home help would be provided by the mainstream services.

The quality of relationships between organisers of hospital discharge schemes and mainstream services was vital for smooth and integrated provision of services to clients. In authorities A and B relationships were good because there was 'give and take' in home help resources between the two types of service. In authorities C and D resources were already thinly stretched, which tended to make some mainstream organisers resent the extra demands which had been stimulated by the existence of their authorities' schemes.

Table 4.5
Intensity of Provision for Clients to be Provided and Referral to Hospital Discharge Scheme/Mainstream Service

Intensity of provision	Dept A		Dept B		Dept C		Dept D	All Depts
	HD (147)	MS (77)	HD (75)	MS (51)	HD *	MS (62)	all refs (12)	all refs* (424)
	%	%	%	%	%	%	N	%
(a) Low intensity/low spread	63	78	87	73		82	(1)	72
(b) Low intensity/med spread	18	16	4	4		5	(1)	11
(c) High intensity/med spread	5	6	9	10		11	(10)	10
(d) Full spread	14	–	–	14		2	–	7

HD—Hospital Discharge   Scheme MS—Mainstream Service
* The proportion of missing records for provision is particularly high for referrals to department C for reasons discussed in the text. These referrals have, therefore, been excluded completely from this table.
(a) 0.5 to 4 hours service over 1–2 days.
(b) 0.5 to 4 hours service over 3–5 days.
(c) 4.5 or more hours service over 3–5 days.
(d) Any number of hours over 6–7 days.

Intensity of home help service

Organisers gave information about the number of hours and the number of days they anticipated home help would be given to the patient during the week following discharge from hospital. For the purposes of discussing intensity of service, referrals to the hospital discharge scheme in authority C have been excluded as these were all referred on to mainstream services. In authorities A, B and D, the monitoring card showed that home help was to be provided or recommended for four hundred and twenty four people and information was available about the number of hours and days on which it was anticipated home help was to be provided.

As Table 4.5 shows, it was anticipated that 72% of these four hundred and twenty four people would receive between one half to four hours help on one to two days during the first week of their care. It was anticipated that only around 7% of clients would receive care on six or seven days per week, which would include the weekend, but there were great variations between groups of organisers. The hospital discharge scheme in department A anticipated providing care on six or seven days per week to 14% of their clients, as did the mainstream service in department B.

There were two different organisational influences which enabled these two groups of organisers to provide greater cover on more days per week. In the discharge scheme in authority A home help workers sometimes worked in tandem with mainstream home helps. This enabled more days per week to be covered. One fifth of the clients referred to this organiser were to be helped by both hospital discharge and mainstream home helps who shared 'cover' during the week.

By contrast, mainstream service organisers in department B could only provide care on six or seven days per week because they had identified and classified a group of their existing clientele as lower priority. When the need for an intensive service arose, either on the basis of several hours or several days per week, home help to the lower priority clients on existing caseloads was either discontinued or decreased. The effects of such arrangements on 'lower priority' clients were not monitored and caused anxiety to organisers.

The high number of referrals in departments C and D on which it was difficult to obtain accurate information on home help input means we are unable to comment on the planned home help provision in these departments.

Eligibility for interview study

Referrals which were deemed eligible for inclusion in the group from which a random sample of seventy people were to be selected for interview had to satisfy three criteria.
They had to be:

- aged 75 years or older;
- in hospital at or prior to referral;
- provided with home help on discharge from hospital.

Sixteen per cent of all 2,035 referrals met these three criteria and were therefore eligible (Table 4.6).

Age and gender of the interview sample

Comparing the interview sample with monitored referrals which were not selected but yet were eligible for inclusion in the study (in that the three criteria of age, hospitalisation and provision of home help were met), age was very similar. Eligible but not selected referrals showed an average age of 82.8 years overall with almost no difference between men and women, whereas for the interview sample the average age overall was 82.3 years.

Women accounted for 75% of the sixty nine cases in the interview sample, compared with 73% of all 2,035 monitored referrals and 74% of eligible not selected cases. Women in the sample had an age range of 75 to 97 years, with an average age of 82.6 years. The remaining seventeen men in the sample had ages ranging from 75 to 91 years, with an average age of 81.6 years. Overall, there were six men and nineteen women aged 85 years or more.

The methods of selecting and interviewing for the small sample are discussed further in chapter 5.

Table 4.6
Eligibility for Interview Study by Department and Referral to Hospital Discharge Scheme/Mainstream Service

Eligibility	Dept A		Dept B		Dept C		Dept D	ALL DEPTS	Depts A B C	
	HD (152)	MS (170)	HD (148)	MS (105)	HD (437)	MS (181)	all refs (842)	all refs (2035)	HD (737)	MS (456)
Client:	%	%	%	%	%	%	%	%	%	%
(1) Aged 75+	59	62	54	63	65	61	74	67	61	62
(no record)	1	19	1	6	1	6	2	3	1	11
(2) In hospital prior to referral	99	25	99	31	99	35	98	83	99	30
(no record)	1	20	–	–	0	2	1	2	0	8
(3) Home Help to be provided	96	49	57	64	5	34	19	31	34	47
(no record)	1	31	9	3	72	14	81	54	45	18
All 3 criteria met—eligible	57	9	31	20	3	9	14	16	20	11

HD—Hospital Discharge Scheme   MS—Mainstream Service
Missing records have not been excluded when calculating percentages. See text for discussion about the high proportion of missing records relating to provision.

Summary in the context of community care

The rates of referrals to schemes and mainstream home help services were influenced by differences in organisation and procedures. Two fifths of the referrals to organisers in the four local authorities which were monitored were made to the organiser of the hospital discharge scheme in authority D. This was because all people who required home help after their discharge from hospital were referred to her. At least fifteen hospitals served the population of this London authority. The high referral rate to this organiser indicates the size of the potential demand for home help on discharge from hospital.

Most referrals to organisers were made after the patient had left hospital or on the day of discharge. Organisers of schemes in authorities A and B received a slightly longer notice of discharge, which probably reflected their more regular contacts with ward staff.

Two thirds of all referrals which were monitored related to people aged 75 years or older, three quarters lived alone, and women outnumbered men by 3:1. There were few referrals of elderly people from minority ethnic groups in any of the authorities studied.

Only half the people referred for home help were considered by organisers to need this service, but there was

43

considerable variation between schemes and mainstream services. Proportionately more people referred to hospital discharge schemes than to mainstream home help services were subsequently assessed as needing the service.

Although hospital social workers were the most frequent sources of referral in two authorities (B and D) they did not give organisers longer notice of discharge, nor were there apparent differences in the characteristics of the people they referred.

Hospitalisation was also a factor in one third of the referrals for home help made to the mainstream home help services which were monitored. This meant that mainstream organisers, ideally, also required good liaison with the hospitals who requested their services.

An apparently high proportion of inappropriate referrals to organisers of mainstream services was frustrating to the people being referred, wasted the time of the organisers and probably reflected an inaccurate awareness of referrers of the roles of the home help service.

The amount of home help planned for those assessed to need it was relatively low. It was anticipated by organisers that nearly three quarters of the people referred to them would receive up to four hours help spread over one or two days during the week following their hospital discharge. Hospital discharge schemes tended to plan for a higher level of provision than did mainstream services.

Chapter 5

Methods of selecting and interviewing the sample and analysing the data

Sample selection

During a period of six months seventy cases were selected at random from referrals identified as eligible for the research. Approximately equal numbers were selected from hospital discharge schemes and mainstream referrals. People were not excluded from the sample on the grounds of particular illnesses or disability or because they were reported to be 'confused'.

Interviewing

Interviewers

The nine interviewers were hand-picked for their experience, insight and interest in the situations of elderly people and for their ability to understand the pressures on home help organisers. Five were qualified social workers and one of these had previous experience as a home help and as an assistant organiser. Two other interviewers had worked in the home help service, one as an organiser and the other as a principal officer. For obvious reasons, no interviewer interviewed people in a local authority in which they had been previously employed.

Making contact and obtaining permissions

A system was established for obtaining the agreement of the organiser for each elderly person to be included in the research. The organiser then asked the elderly person for permission to pass the name and address to the research interviewer. A summary of research aims was available on request.

Interviewers were responsible for contacting each elderly person to make an appointment for the interview. The ways in which initial contacts were made were influenced by advice from the organiser who had met the elderly person. A formal letter on headed paper which described the purposes of the research was appropriate for some, but was not a successful way of making initial contact with others as it made some elderly people apprehensive. However, brief introductory informal letters, telephone calls or visits were always followed by a letter on headed paper to confirm the appointment. Interviewers carried identity cards which contained a photograph of themselves, a reproduction of the headed paper used and names and telephone numbers of NISW research unit staff to whom queries could be addressed. Interviewers were required to show these cards to everybody they interviewed, although they were seldom asked for them. A summary of achieved interviews is shown in Table 5.1.

Order of interviews

Each interviewer was responsible for the full set of six interviews on each case, that is with the elderly person, their carer, the organiser and the home help. On each case the order of interviews two weeks after discharge was home help organiser, elderly person and their main carer; ten weeks later the order was elderly person, their carer and their home help. A 'carer' was defined as the relative or friend who gave the elderly person the most personal care or who was in most frequent contact on a daily basis. At the end of the first interview elderly people were asked to identify such carers and to give permission for the interviewer to make contact with them.

Length of interviews

Most interviews with elderly people lasted two or more hours. It was obvious that many people valued an opportunity for a detailed and reflective discussion of their situation and appreciated being asked for their opinions.

Problems with interviews

More than half of the elderly people selected for interview either did not have any carer, apart from their home help, or were reluctant to give their permission for their carer to be interviewed. When permission was refused by elderly people most of their reasons were either because they did not want further demands to be made on their carer or because the person identified did not perceive themselves as a 'carer'. Friendly visits from neighbours or friends which were based on a relationship of equality were important and some elderly people were apprehensive about identifying themselves as people requiring help. Sometimes they were also unwilling to be 'talked about by their neighbours'.

There was some interviewer bias which influenced whether or not interviews with carers were obtained. Some interviewers were more forthright than others in obtaining permission from elderly people. However, when interviews were held with friends who did not see themselves as 'carers' it was clear that the doubts of some elderly people were well-founded and tact had to be exercised over parts of the questionnaires which were inappropriate.

Table 5.1
Summary of Achieved Interviews

Interview with:	2 weeks after discharge	12 weeks after discharge
Elderly person	69	63
Carer	28	32
Home help organiser	71*	–
Home help		68
Totals	168	163
Interviewers' evaluation schedules		70

Notes:

1. In 7 cases, the first elderly person's interview was not followed up at 12 weeks. Thus 62 cases are used to present findings in the chapters on 'outcome'. In one other case, only one interview was obtained and this was at 12 weeks.
2. With respect to carers, there were interviews neither at 2 weeks nor at 12 weeks in 38 cases; twenty seven interviews were achieved both at 2 weeks and 12 weeks; in five cases there was no interview at 2 weeks but there was one at 12 weeks; in one case an interview took place at 2 weeks but not at 12 weeks.
3. In all but three cases, an interview with the organiser at 2 weeks after discharge was followed by an interview with the home help at 12 weeks.
4. The 71* cases include one elderly person who at 12 weeks had become the carer to her disabled sister. She was interviewed both as an elderly person at 2 weeks and as a carer at 12 weeks. Her disabled sister was given a case number.

Interviewing procedure—12 weeks after discharge

Further interviews were not sought with those elderly people who had been admitted to permanent residential care during the intervening period or with those who had been readmitted to hospital for an extended stay. Two elderly people died before they could be interviewed for a second time, and two others were admitted to a hospital or nursing home. One elderly person declined to be interviewed a second time.

When second interviews with elderly people were not possible, interviews were still sought with their carers and with their home helps. When there had been a change of home help from the person giving help immediately after the elderly person was discharged from hospital, interviews were sought with the home help currently in closest contact with the elderly person. In a few cases the current home help was being provided on a temporary basis because the 'regular' home help was absent. Efforts were then made to interview the 'regular' home help even although this meant making a request for an interview while a home help was away sick or on annual leave. In most cases home helps were interviewed during their normal working hours and the time they spent on the interview entered on their time sheets in the usual way.

For geographical convenience interviewers were divided into two groups. Each group met with the researcher every month.

Contents of questionnaires

Questionnaires were designed to enable some comparisons to be made between the views of respondents at each of these two points in time and between the situations of elderly people and their carers 2 and 12 weeks after discharge. The contents of these questionnaires is shown in Figure 5.1.

Analysing the data

Questionnaires contained pre-coded questions which were analysed using the SPSS statistical package. As this was a feasibility study and the sample for interviews was small, statistically significant findings were not expected.

Interviews with this sample of people provided opportunities for some comparison of the perspectives of the elderly person, their carer, their home help organiser and their home help at two points in time after each elderly person's discharge from hospital.

It was anticipated that interviews with a small sample would also enable us to explore changes in the situations of these elderly people between two and twelve weeks after their discharge from hospital. During this process it was hoped that areas in which change occurred could be identified in preparation for the evaluation of change in further research with a larger sample.

Factual changes such as changes in living groups, accommodation or the amount of home help provision could be classified and recorded without undue difficulty. However, it was also necessary to explore ways of monitoring change in more complex areas such as physical disability, morale and dementia.

Physical disability

It was important to use identical questions to all respondents about each elderly person's abilities and self-care difficulties. Pilot work had shown that questions to home help organisers had to be brief. Partly for this reason it was decided to use the Guttman scale to describe disability, as this had been used in other studies of elderly people, for example Arber *et al.*, 1988.

Figure 5.1 Contents of Questionnaires for Interviews

	2 weeks after discharge EP	2 weeks after discharge Carer	2 weeks after discharge HHO	12 weeks after discharge EP	12 weeks after discharge Carer	12 weeks after discharge HH
In relation to EP:						
Hospitalisation	*	*				
Discharge	*	*	*			*
Arriving home	*	*				
Household/personal history	*			*		
Network-relatives/friends	*			*		
Relationship to EP		*			*	*
Accommodation	*	*		*	*	*
Self care difficulties (incl. sensory problems)	*	*	*	*	*	*
Daily routine/personal care	*	*		*	*	
Quality of life	*	*		*	*	
Care and services	*	*		*	*	
The home help	*	*		*		
Weekly time table of carers and visitors	*	*	planned HH prov.	*	*	
Home help tasks	*	*	planned tasks	*	*	*
In relation to carer:						
Daily regime caring for EP		*				
Personal burden on carer		*			*	
Other:						
General changes since last interview				*	*	
Communication and collaboration						*
Support and training for home helps						*

The Guttman scale is: This person usually manages to:

Get up and down steps and stairs.
Get around the house.
Get in and out of bed.
Cut their toenails themselves.
Bath, shower or wash all over.
Go out and walk down the road.

Each response is coded in one of three ways: 'on own without difficulty', 'on own but difficult', 'cannot do or only with help from somebody'. The replies are weighted and scored.

In addition, elderly people and their carers were asked to report the elderly person's degrees of difficulty in relation to a list of eighteen self-care tasks. This list of tasks had been developed and used in a national study by a colleague in the National Institute for Social Work Research Unit (SSI, 1990).

Analysis of the findings of this research showed that the Guttman scale was useful to compare our sample in broad terms with other characteristics. However, because the researcher had under-estimated the disability of this group of very old people, three fifths of the sample were at the extreme end of the Guttman scale, which classified them as 'very severely disabled'. This meant that further deterioration in this group could not be measured using the Guttman scale.

It was found that the more detailed list of eighteen self-care tasks produced a more sensitive analysis of the areas in which change did or did not occur.

Daily Routine

In order to assess whether the help elderly people received was appropriate to their difficulties with mobility and self care it was necessary to understand not only what these difficulties were but the times of day or night they usually occurred. The habits of a life-time in domestic regimes were likely to persist. For these reasons elderly people were asked about their 'usual' daily routine and whether this had changed since their hospitalisation. These questions explored 'normal' activities such as what time the elderly person liked to get up and go to bed, to have something to eat, the time of day they liked to doze and which part of the day they most looked forward to and why.

When difficulties were mentioned, interviewers were asked to explore the specific causes of these, such as pain, weakness or stiffness. Whether or not appropriate aids and adaptations had been provided and were used was also noted. Their carer was also asked about the elderly person's routine so that replies could be compared.

Elderly people and their carers responded to this detailed questioning about the elderly person's daily pattern of activity with enthusiasm. It was interesting that all the elderly people in the sample described a daily routine to which they adhered despite their disabilities.

Dementia and 'confusion'

Another colleague in the Research Unit of the National Institute for Social Work has developed a list of six questions and has defined a score above which the possibility of dementia exists and psychiatric diagnosis should be sought. These questions were designed to be used by home helps and have now been tested widely and used successfully in two national studies (Levin *et al.*, 1989). We included these questions in questionnaires to home help organisers and home helps and in the evaluation schedules which interviewers were required to complete.

The questions were: Does ---------- have noticeable problems in:

Remembering recent events?
Working out how to do basic everyday tasks?
Knowing the time?
Knowing where he/she is?
Correctly naming people he/she sees regularly?
Keeping in touch with a conversation?

A score of 1 is given for each affirmative reply. Overall scores of 1–2 are classified as mild cognitive loss, 3–4 as moderate cognitive loss and 5–6 as severe cognitive loss. The scale is designed for simple preliminary screening and its purpose is to identify those people for whom a further medical or psychiatric assessment might be desirable.

Analysis of data from the sample showed that these questions accurately identified six people who showed symptoms of possible dementia, which was the purpose for which this score was developed. Three of the six people whose score indicated possible dementia had a physical disability or illness which might affect cognitive loss. These conditions included a severe stroke and recent brain surgery. It must be emphasised that these people had not had a psychiatric assessment. However, it was clear that any change over time in this score had to be interpreted with caution in this sample.

Morale

The importance of their morale and quality of life was emphasised by elderly people during interviews. Each elderly person was asked to respond to a series of questions which had been developed by Bird and her colleagues (1987) which had been shown to identify possible clinical depression in the elderly which indicated need for a psychiatric assessment. The replies to these questions were scored from 0–12 with depression indicated by any score of 6 or higher. Comparison of the scores derived from these questions with the content of interview schedules indicated that these scores appeared to distinguish reliably those who might be depressed from those who were not. The replies of twenty five (35%) of the elderly people who were interviewed resulted in a morale score of 6 or higher, which indicated possible depression in this group.

Care Networks

It was important to classify and compare the total care network of each person in the sample at two points in time after discharge. The total network included contacts with relatives, friends and neighbours as well as with statutory services. Information about networks was obtained in three ways.

First, elderly people were asked about their environmental 'roots' and how long they had lived at their present address. Secondly, they were asked to list all the relatives and friends who were alive and important to them. General information was obtained about the location of all these friends and relatives, so that it could be classified as 'local' (i.e within 50 miles or one day's journey), elsewhere in Britain or abroad. The nature of the contact of these people with each elderly person was also recorded. Although we were primarily interested in personal contacts, regular telephone calls or letters were also indicators of how active these caring relationships were. For example, the son of one lady lived in Scotland but she said *'He phones me every evening. He would always come if I sent for him'*.

Thirdly, a grid was devised which divided the seven days of a 'usual' week into four periods of time, 8.00 a.m to noon, noon to 4.00 p.m, 4.00 p.m to 8.00 p.m and 8.00 p.m to 8.00 a.m. All visitors, including the home help, were recorded in this grid. Interviewers were asked to check especially for visitors in the early morning, evening and during weekends. 'Special' events which made any day different from other days were recorded such as *'every other weekend my daughter collects me in her car and takes me to lunch at her place'*.

These details enabled comparisons to be made between the types of difficulties and when these occurred with whether anybody was available to help. For example, an elderly man who had had a stroke had difficulty in dressing himself but he said *'I've always been used to getting up by 7.00 a.m. The home help comes at 9.30 a.m and she finishes me off. She tells me to wait in bed for her but I feel I can't hang about in bed that long'*. Although the number and types of people visiting can be counted and analysed, the data from this study does not provide information about the quality and contents of all these contacts. Experience of this sample and awareness of current national developments in community care has strengthened the researchers' convictions that it is important to continue to search for a simple way of recording and classifying care networks so that changes in the match or mismatch of services may be evaluated.

Motivation and key facts of social history

People in the sample were a cross-section of the population who happened to be in a particular age group and who had been in hospital. Some were highly educated; some were very intelligent and articulate; others were not. When asked about their backgrounds, occupations and past experiences, many of these elderly people described in detail their history and achievements, the help they had given to others, their pride in their children, their hobbies, skills and interests and their spiritual beliefs. Some of the people who were interviewed had experienced a major crisis in their lives during hospitalisation. Their responses to such challenges can only be adequately understood in the context of their strengths as well as in the context of their disabilities.

Questionnaires often contained verbatim comments from elderly people about their pre-retirement occupations and experiences and about more recent events before their hospitalisation. This information was not obtained systematically and so has not been analysed in detail, but the impression was gained that to do so might provide clues as to why some very old disabled people fought for recovery after hospitalisation whereas others seemed more quickly defeated.

There were obvious historical facts of importance, such as bereavements. Apart from these, it seemed that, for example, the nature of past skills and activities, attitudes towards their homes and the quality of their memories were matters which either supported the rehabilitation of these elderly people or eroded their recovery. This feasibility study suggests that further and more systematic research into such influences on recovery might be rewarding.

Basic characteristics of the respondents interviewed

The sixty nine people interviewed two weeks after discharge consisted of forty who had been referred to one of the four hospital discharge schemes and twenty nine who had been referred to a mainstream home help service.

As Table 5.2 shows, the age distribution of these respondents was similar to the age distribution within the three hundred and seventeen referrals who had been identified as 'eligible' from the sampling frame of all monitored referrals.

All except seven of the sixty nine people who were interviewed lived alone. This included seven of the eight people who were aged ninety years or older. The oldest person living alone, who was also the oldest person in the sample, was ninety seven years old.

Table 5.2
Age Group of Elderly People Interviewed Compared with all 'Eligible' Referrals

Age group (yrs)	All 'eligible' referrals (N=317)	Respondents interviewed (N=69)
	%	%
75–79	32	41
80–84	31	23
85–89	27	23
90+	10	13

Summary in the context of community care

This chapter has described the approaches made to elderly people and the nature of the interviews with them. The scales adopted for measuring physical disability, confusion and morale were also described. The achieved interview sample of sixty nine elderly people was found to be similar, with respect to age and gender to the set of monitored referrals which were 'eligible' but not selected.

All the elderly people who were interviewed described a daily routine which they still tried to follow, however great their physical disability. Detailed systematic questions about this routine were found to be worth asking, for they pinpointed the times when help was most needed and the tasks for which it was required.

It was found that the word 'carer' had to be used with caution with both elderly people and with some friends and neighbours. Half the people in the sample either had no carers or else they refused permission for them to be interviewed. These refusals were respected. When permission was given reluctantly and carers who identified themselves as 'friends or neighbours' were interviewed, it was found that some did not define themselves as a 'carer'. The implications of being described as a 'carer' for the first time appeared to make some people apprehensive, especially if they had been unaware of the importance of their relationship to the elderly person and the extent to which the elderly person was depending upon their help.

This finding is important for community care, for use of the term 'carers', whether by practitioners in the health and social services or by researchers, may not match the way in which such 'carers' see themselves.

Carers who are are friends and neighbours may willingly help an elderly person but may be reluctant for the formal responsibility implied by the official term of 'carer' to be thrust upon them.

Although useful information about elderly people's care networks was obtained, the researchers felt that the essential quality and content of care networks remained obscure and that further study was required.

Similarly, motivation towards recovery appeared to be more closely related to the personalities and social histories of these elderly people than to the natures of their illnesses or disability. This research was not designed to explore these important areas.

Chapter 6

Home help organisers' views of the discharge processes

Introduction

All the organisers of hospital discharge schemes and mainstream services who participated in this research had had the experience of receiving referrals from a hospital. Much previous research has explored issues of discharge from hospital from the perspectives of patients. Before doing this we sought to document the organisers' experiences of the seventy referrals in this study.

Twenty five organisers were interviewed and each was asked about at least one case in the sample. Six of these organisers were managing four different hospital discharge schemes in separate local authorities and the rest were working in mainstream home help services. Before meeting the research interviewers, all organisers had had contacts with the people in the sample.

Organisational influences

The different types of service which organisers were operating influenced the speed and extent of home help service they were empowered to provide. As described earlier, three hospital discharge schemes were staffed with teams of home helps who were accountable to the organisers. In scheme A, the organiser was based in the large district general hospital from which most of her referrals were received. In scheme B, the senior organiser and her two assistants spent much of their time in two local hospitals, although their work base was in a local authority resource centre. In scheme D the organiser was based in offices adjacent to a social services area office. She received referrals from at least fifteen hospitals and referred four fifths of these on to mainstream services. Scheme C differed from the other three in that the organiser had no team of home helps, and therefore had to refer patients on to mainstream home help services after making her assessments.

The quality of referrals to organisers

Simple criteria for a 'good referral' were adopted, arising out of our previous pilot work and from discussion with organisers. These three criteria seemed implicit in the more detailed guidelines in the Department of Health booklet *Discharge of Patients from Hospital, (1989)*.

These were that a minimum standard for a 'good' referral process should include three components:

- – there should be adequate notice given to the organiser of a patient's discharge;
- – the organiser should consider that sufficient information was given to her at referral for her to proceed with her assessment;
- – the organiser should consider that the request for her home help/home care services was realistic.

Notice of discharge to organisers

There were stark differences in the length of notice of discharge which organisers would like *ideally* and the notice which their experiences had led them to expect. Organisers planned the work loads of their home helps one week ahead and so ideally one week's notice of a 'new' referral would fit this routine. Most organisers thought that even two days' notice of a patient's discharge would be very convenient.

Whether or not notice of discharge was said to be 'adequate' reflects whether it had been possible for the organiser to provide a service within the time allowed.

Table 6.1 shows that organisers considered that they had received adequate notice of discharge for four fifths of the cases in the sample. Closer investigation of the content of interviews suggests that replies by organisers reflected their relatively low expectations of the quality of referral procedures. Notice of discharge was often 'adequate' because the organisers made it so.

Table 6.1 Organisers' Opinions of Adequate Notice of Discharge and Timing of Notice of Discharge to Elderly People

Organisers' opinions of notice of discharge	Timing of notice to elderly people	
	Same day/ day before (26)*	More than a day before (39)*
Was notice adequate?	N	N
yes	18	31
not completely/no	8	8

* In five cases there were missing records for length of notice and these have been excluded.

If a referral was made on the day of discharge some organisers would reorganise their other work, if this was possible, in order immediately to assess the patient and arrange the services which were necessary. It was usually when a referral was made after discharge that the organiser objected on behalf of the patient.

Such modest expectations of how much notice of discharge was 'adequate' were reflected in comparison of organisers' opinions with the length of notice of discharge which the elderly person stated they had actually received.

Table 6.1 also shows that a maximum of one day's notice of discharge was given to the elderly patients for two fifths of the referrals in the sample, yet organisers considered this was adequate for a third of this group. Such brief notice of discharge was unsatisfactory primarily because it could cause unnecessary suffering to the patient and not because it was also inconsiderate to organisers.

A discharge scheme organiser said:

> 'I happened to call into the ward and the charge nurse told me they had sent her (the patient) home that morning because they needed the bed, but the nurse said the patient would be alright because they had given her a packed lunch to take with her. I was worried so I called in to see her on my way home from work. I don't know what would have happened if I had not called. She had no food or milk and was feeling too weak and tired to get into bed or into the kitchen. She had plenty of neighbours and friends to help, but they did not know she was home. She had no phone and was too weak to go out to them.'

Discharges on a Friday evening or just before the long Christmas break were exceptional, but they were mentioned as problems by organisers in relation to three people in the sample who lived alone and who lacked close contact with friends or relatives.

Information given to organisers

Although all the local authorities in which the research took place had referral forms, the extent to which these forms were completed depended on the referrer and on the degree of pressure in different types of wards. Mostly, it seemed that obtaining comprehensive information depended on the skill and experience of the person taking the referral. Most referrals were made by telephone, as Table 6.2 shows, although organisers had sometimes had preliminary discussions with ward staff. As mentioned earlier, it was evident that experienced home help clerks were important influences in obtaining full information over the telephone. This usually included the patient's name, address and age, the reason for their hospital admission, the name of their GP and whether they lived alone and why they were considered to need home help.

However, some referrals to organisers contained very brief and sometimes inaccurate information. There were even examples of an organiser being given an inaccurate address for a patient. It

Table 6.2
How Referrals to
Home Help
Organisers were
Made

How referral made	(N=70)
Telephone call	54
Social work duty system	5
During ward contact	3
Home help clerk	2
Other	6

was not unusual for a referral to consist of a message such as: *'Mrs A being discharged today. Needs home help'*. Lack of adequate information at referral could place some elderly people in serious jeopardy and most organisers gave unsolicited examples of this happening.

Information considered essential by organisers

Most referrals concerned elderly people living alone. For this group especially, the information which organisers considered essential at referral included who had the key to the elderly person's home, whether or not an elderly person was able to get in and out of their bed and their chair, whether they were able to make themselves a hot drink and could reach their lavatory or commode without undue difficulty or risk. Organisers said that all too often such basic information could be inaccurate or incomplete.

> *'Nobody knew there was one step down to the kitchen and the lavatory was upstairs—so there she was sitting in her chair stranded. If I had not been able to get in I don't know what would have happened to her'.*

Gaps in information to organisers

Failure to keep organisers informed of changes in discharge arrangements, especially after they had arranged for services to be provided quickly despite short notice of discharge, resulted in wasted time, could sour professional relationships and reduced motivation for quick response on the next similar referral.

> *'They told me that she had nobody and could do very little for herself, so we (the organiser and the home help) kept going round on the day she was coming home. Nobody told us her discharge had been cancelled and she had been moved onto another ward. When she did come home I found she had two daughters who lived up the road and several neighbours who were always popping in'.*

Medical information

It seemed that organisers were seldom given information about the possible side-effects of the medication prescribed to a patient. This could have serious consequences, especially where the home help was the main carer of a confused elderly person. Experienced organisers, and especially those in regular contact with ward sisters through hospital discharge schemes, said they usually asked about medication and its effects. The extent to which home helps were involved in helping patients to take medication varied between authorities. This was a 'grey' area of responsibility around which strong feelings prevailed.

Direct questions were not asked on this topic, but the impression was gained that organisers encountered very varied attitudes from medical staff about the medical information with which they could be entrusted. Passing such information to a home help organiser or to a home help without the patient's knowledge raised ethical issues. Most organisers considered that if they were to work effectively as part of a patient's care network they had to be appropriately informed. However, they considered that possessing information, for example about terminal illness, required training and continued support in how to use it. Schemes' organisers, who were in frequent contact with ward staff seldom had difficulty in acquiring appropriate medical information.

Information from trial visits

Twelve (17%) of the seventy patients in the sample had been home for a 'trial' visit, usually with an occupational therapist and sometimes a hospital nurse, so that their practical needs could be assessed and appropriate services arranged. Although home help was expected to be a crucial part of this care plan, home help organisers had been present with only two of the twelve patients who had trial visits home. Organisers were not automatically informed when a trial visit home had been arranged nor were they invited to attend. The researcher gained the impression that this was partly because organisers were ambivalent. They were already hard-pressed to get through the volume of work they had and one or two hours spent on a trial visit was an extra heavy demand, especially on organisers who were working alone or who lacked clerical help. However, most organisers said they would like to attend trial home visits or, given adequate notice of discharge, to send the home help who would be visiting the elderly person after their discharge. This would enable the elderly person and their relatives to meet and plan with the home help in the context of the home environment and in collaboration with other carers.

Realistic expectations of home help services

For all except four of the seventy cases in the sample organisers said that the referrers had realistic expectations of their services. However, in one in three cases organisers said that there were services they would like to be able to provide but could not. In general, organisers felt they were providing the minimal essential service and not the cover which was actually required. *'Ideally she needs us there every day'*. The need for a late evening service and, to some extent, an earlier morning service was raised by several organisers, as was the wish that home helps had more time to take elderly people out for short walks, or wheel them out to do their own shopping or to collect their pension. *'Home helps don't have time to talk to people enough'*

Charges

Although organisers said that charges for services had not affected their assessments, charges did sometimes affect the amount and type of service provided. This constraint arose especially when regular surveillance was required.

> *'Some people need somebody just to pop in to make sure they are alright, but if they have been assessed to pay full cost you are supposed to charge them even for a ten minute visit'.*

Sometimes home helps were paying extra informal visits to clients they knew already and who were especially at risk and isolated from other carers. In such circumstances some organisers turned a blind eye to loopholes in the system.

> *'We are supposed to charge £.... per hour. If she (the home help) pops in for 10–20 minutes that's not an hour, so we don't charge her'.*

However, the risks involved in such delinquent behaviour exacerbated the anxiety and concern of organisers and home helps already operating a thinly stretched service. They had to implement policies about priorities and constraints on service provision, but the emotional cost to them was the awareness of individual elderly people who were struggling to care for themselves.

The amount of home help planned at referral

When each referral in the sample was received organisers were asked by the researcher to record the number of hours per week and the number of days per week they anticipated home help would be needed and provided. These predictions were subsequently compared with the hours and days home help had actually been provided during the two weeks following each elderly person's discharge from hospital. It was found that the predictions of organisers at referral were accurate in only 29% of cases. Usually this was because they had over-estimated the hours and days of subsequent provision. In part this reflected stress on home help resources, but discrepancies also arose because the nature and extent of a person's informal care network did not become fully apparent until after he or she had arrived home and home help had started. Such difficulty in forward planning has implications for the roles of the care managers which are envisaged in the NHS and Community Care Act.

Hospital discharge schemes and mainstream services

Taking the three criteria described earlier, organisers who were managing hospital discharge schemes were more likely to receive 'good' referrals than were organisers in mainstream services. This reflected the closer collaboration between these organisers with hospital personnel and especially with ward sisters. It also reflected the greater confidence of these organisers to discuss with referrers how much notice of discharge would be required for the provision of integrated care for individual patients. They also had an opportunity to resolve any difficulties over referral procedures which might arise between them and hospital personnel. This access was not so easily available to mainstream organisers.

Three quarters of the referrals received by hospital discharge schemes, but less than half of those to mainstream services satisfied all three criteria for 'good' referral. All referrals to discharge schemes were said to include realistic expectations of the discharge service. 'Adequate' information at referral and notice of discharge were also more often reported and organisers of schemes received longer notice of discharge.

Organisers of discharge schemes received two or more days' notice of referral for two thirds of the referrals in the sample compared with half of the referrals made to mainstream organisers. Sometimes they were able to re-negotiate a discharge date if they and the patient required this. However, numbers in sub-groups were very small.
small.

Hospital discharge schemes, especially those in authorities A and B, were geared to a quick response and were equipped for this. All the home helps in these schemes had cars and bleeps which enabled the organiser to be in immediate contact and the home help to respond quickly. This meant that some service could be provided with even a few hours' notice of discharge. For example, in the words of one organiser of a discharge scheme:

> *'If a very disabled person is being discharged the same day as the referral is made, I go to see the person on the ward and find out what will be needed immediately. I bleep the best worker for that particular situation and if equipment such as a chemical commode is needed I ask her to go to the stores and collect it in her car. She will visit as soon as the patient arrives home and will make sure that he or she is warm and safe and has food provided. The home help will visit again the next day and I will also visit to do a further assessment of the patient and plan the help we should give'.*

**Summary in the
context of
community care**

In general, organisers said they received 'adequate' notice of discharge, but it seemed organisers had low expectations of the quality of referrals made to them and had adapted their own routines and the work loads of their home helps to these conditions.

The marked lack of assertiveness of organisers towards referrers who made poor referrals appeared to be influenced by their feeling that:

- home help organisers lacked professional status;
- some of their managers were too preoccupied with other pressures to take a proactive stance about poor referrals to home help organisers;
- basic criteria for 'good' referrals were not established and acknowledged by relevant personnel in health and social services.

Information to organisers at referral seldom included medical information or essential details of a patient's home environment and ability to care for themselves. Organisers were seldom invited to attend 'trial' home visits which had been arranged by an occupational therapist prior to a patient's discharge.

Organisers of mainstream home help services had to plan to provide a minimum essential level of service to discharged patients, whereas schemes organisers were able to be more flexible in response to client need.

Discharge schemes home helps were equipped for quick response by being provided with bleeps, a car allowance and having more extensive hours of employment.

Some organisers were constrained by charges to elderly people who had been assessed to pay maximum cost.

In informal conversations with the researcher organisers expressed passionate concern about the risk caused to some elderly people through inadequate discharge procedures.

Chapter 7

Elderly people's views of their hospitalisation and preparation for discharge

Two weeks after their discharge sixty nine of the seventy patients in the sample were interviewed. Although she was seen, it proved impossible to converse with one patient, who was seriously ill in bed, extensively paralysed and without speech.

Constraints in interviews with elderly people arising from poor memory and response

Issues over assessing confusion and the score we used have been discussed earlier. Just over a quarter of the sample (27%) appeared to have minor cognitive loss, and eleven people (16% of the sample) appeared to have cognitive loss which was moderate or severe.

Three people in the sample of seventy scored 5 or 6, which indicated severe cognitive loss. One of these was the seriously ill lady just described. Another had had major brain surgery and was being cared for by her husband. The third person was a widow, living alone in some distress and chaos. There was no evidence that she had received a psychiatric assessment or that a community psychiatric nurse was in contact with her.

The score indicated that eight other people, who were all living alone, had moderate cognitive loss. Subsequent interviews confirmed this. However, the causes are open to question. Four people in this group had, in addition, a physically disabling condition; one had multiple sclerosis, another Parkinsons disease, one had had a major stroke and the fourth was terminally ill with cancer and died within weeks of discharge. A fifth lady was said to have become 'confused' since surgery on her hip. There was no evidence of psychiatric assessment of any of these people.

Interviewers were able to conduct some part of the interviews with all of these apparently 'confused' people, but the contents of these interviews were later scrutinised carefully to ensure that the responses of these elderly people were compatible with the rest of the sample. Some responses were missing. For example, some people could not remember how long they had been in hospital nor how long ago they had been discharged. Other responses were improbable. For example, one lady said she had been sent home from hospital on a milk float and another that she had come home by bus. In both circumstances these modes of transport home were unlikely. Replies to other types of questions were often articulate. For example, questions concerning feelings about their carers and about the quality of their own lives received articulate and sometimes insightful replies. There were logical responses to questions about self care difficulties and daily domestic regimes, although in one or two cases interviewers suspected that these elderly people were presenting an unduly rosy picture of their abilities, for example, to cook for themselves or to clean their own homes. One lady, on discharge did not recognise the home help she had had for eighteen years.

Despite these difficulties arising from cognitive loss, the overall logic of many of the replies from these people influenced our decision to include their answers with the rest of the sample and to enter 'can't remember' as a 'no record' in tables. Improbable replies are recorded as 'other'.

Hospitalisation and preparation for discharge

In order to consider the effectiveness of the services provided after discharge from hospital, it is necessary to describe why people entered hospital, some of their experiences during hospitalisation and their views about the process of discharge.

Planned and unplanned admission to hospital

The admission to hospital of over half the people in the sample had not been planned beforehand. Table 7.1 shows that only eleven people (16%) had been admitted from a hospital waiting list. The admission of a further 14 people (20% of the sample) had been planned to the extent that their general practitioner had requested admission. Thirty two people (46% of the sample) had been admitted as an emergency via a casualty department and

**Table 7.1
Type of Admission
to Hospital
(N=69)**

	(N=69)	
	N	%
Planned—on waiting list	11	16
Planned—not on waiting list	14	20
Unplanned—not emergency	8	12
Unplanned—emergency	32	46
Other/no record	4	6

eight people had an unplanned admission in other ways. For example, some had attended an out-patient clinic and had been admitted.

Preparation for an event such as hospitalisation presumably influences the degree to which the experience can be tolerated and accepted. Several studies of the discharge from hospital of elderly patients show that, for a large proportion of respondents, admission to hospital had been unplanned. Nearly 2,000 patients discharged from hospitals were studied in Wales, and it was found that half of these had been admitted as emergencies (Victor, nd). Similarly, 38% of the smaller sample of patients discharged from a hospital in Brighton had also been emergency admissions (Williamson, 1985). In the latter study, a further 23% of patients had prior notice of admission of one week or less. This pattern of either emergency admission or a few days notice was reflected in other work, such as the CCP's programmes in various hospitals in the Midlands.

Reasons for admission

The eleven people in this sample who had been admitted from a hospital waiting list required hospitalisation for a variety of reasons. Three were to have operations for cataract, one had been admitted to provide respite for her carer and the others had required treatments such as hip replacements, a new pacemaker, removal of a gall bladder or investigation of intractable varicose ulcers.

Half of the emergency admissions in our sample arose from a fall. Other accidents or emergencies included road traffic accidents and a diabetic coma.

The hospital admission of a further twenty two old people had, in their estimations, not been an 'emergency' but had not been anticipated either. These 'unplanned' admissions had usually been the result of a GP's visit or a hospital out-patient clinic and included conditions such as pneumonia, bronchitis, two cardiovascular accidents (CVA), haemorrhages of various types, an abscess on a colostomy and other acute infections. This meant that three fifths of the people who were interviewed had not anticipated an admission to hospital and had not planned to leave their homes, pets or possessions.

In view of these precipitous admissions it is not surprising that over three fifths (70%) of the elderly people who were interviewed said they had no idea how long they would remain in hospital when they were first admitted.

Type of treatment and length of hospitalisation

Hospital treatment had included surgery for over one third (38%) of these elderly people, including three people who had had amputations. One quarter of the unplanned admissions had resulted in surgical intervention. Of the people admitted after a fall, two fifths had required surgery for fractures. Table 7.2 shows that planned admissions more frequently required surgery.

Somewhat surprisingly, there were four cases of drug poisoning in this small sample of sixty nine people, which either caused or prolonged the hospital stay. Two emergency admissions had resulted from an adverse reaction to penicillin and a mistaken prescription by a chemist of a diuretic instead of a drug for diabetes which caused a diabetic coma. Two patients said they experienced periods of hallucination in hospital resulting from inappropriate pain killing drugs.

Calculation of the total length of stay in hospital included some people who had been transferred to different wards or different hospitals. Only one in five (22%) of this sample had been in hospital for one week or less. One third (32%) were in hospital for between 8–30 nights. A similar proportion (29%) had been in hospital for between a month and a year. However, of this long-stay group only four people had been in-patients for longer than three months.

Table 7.2
Elderly People Two Weeks After Discharge: Whether Admission to Hospital was Planned and Whether Treatment Included Surgery (N=69*)

Treatment included surgery?	Admission to hospital was:			
	Planned (25)		Unplanned (40)	
	N	%	N	%
Yes	16	62	10	26
No	9	38	30	74

* Includes 4 cases for which type of admission was not recorded. Percentages were calculated excluding a further 2 cases for which treatment was not recorded.

Obviously, the length of time people stayed in hospital depended on the reasons for their admission and the types of treatment they received. In this sample, people who required the removal of cataracts or whose falls had resulted in shocks or bruises only, were in hospital for an average of three days. Where falls had caused fractures necessitating surgery, the average stay in hospital was seven weeks. The people in the sample who were admitted after strokes had, on average, been in hospital for three months, as had those who had varicose ulcers which had been treated with skin grafts.

Table 7.3 shows that one in three people with a planned admission were discharged within one week. Unplanned hospital admissions had resulted in longer stays in hospital (average 41 nights) than admissions which had been planned (average 33 nights). The high proportion of unplanned admissions and extended stays in hospital underlined the extent to which

Table 7.3
Elderly People Two Weeks After Discharge: Whether Admission to Hospital was Planned and Length of Stay in Hospital (N=69*)

Length of stay in hospital	Admission to hospital was:	
	Planned (25)	Unplanned (40)
	%	%
1–7 nights	32	17
8–30 nights	32	30
31–365 nights	20	37
Not known	16	15
**Average number of nights	33	41

* Includes 4 cases for which type of admission was not recorded.
** Base = 21 cases planned and 34 unplanned admissions for which length of stay was known.

accidents, especially falls, may disrupt the lives of elderly people and result in heavy demands on hospital resources. Our sample reflects the high incidence of falls in elderly people, which is well documented in the literature (see, for example, Exton Smith, 1977; Fenton Lewis, 1981; Grimley Evans, 1979; Prudham and Grimley Evans, 1981).

Retrospective feelings and opinions about hospitalisation

Elderly people were asked 'what was good about your treatment' (in hospital) and also 'what was not so good about it'? Nearly all spoke appreciatively about some aspect of their hospital stay. In order of magnitude they had valued the friendships they had made with other patients, the kindness of the nurses, the good food and the skill of their doctors.

When asked what had not been so good about their treatment in hospital very few mentioned pain or discomfort or other physical repercussions of illness as was expected. Nearly all their negative memories were about loss of autonomy and feeling helpless and apprehensive. The central theme of most complaints was lack of information.

Some negative memories reflected the experience of an unplanned admission to hospital. For example, a usually stoical old lady who had fallen and fractured her leg described her anxiety while she waited several hours in the casualty department for a bed to be found. She did not complain about the pain of her fracture but about the helplessness which had suddenly been thrust upon her and the lack of information.

'I didn't know what was going to happen to me—what they were going to do—where I would be sent. I don't want to end up in one of those geriatric places'.

Loss of autonomy on the ward had distressed other elderly people, who had struggled to maintain their independence despite living alone. A diabetic lady who had previously had both legs amputated and who lived alone, tearfully said:

> 'It was a bad experience. My treatment didn't fit in with the ward routine. I knew I had to have breakfast and supper before the insulin injection but they gave me the injection first. They used a different insulin in hospital and reduced the evening dose without telling me. If only they had told the diabetic sister at the hospital that I had come in'.

The issue here was not whether such changes were clinically necessary, but the adverse effect they had upon the self confidence and self determination of an old lady who had tailored her life to a diabetic regime. She lacked the power to make contact with the sister of the diabetic out-patient clinic, whom she trusted and who knew her well.

Discussion before treatment was sometimes felt to be lacking. One old lady who had already been in hospital for several months was advised to have a below-the-knee amputation. The interviewer wrote:

> 'She had about two weeks' warning of the proposed operation and it was clear to her that it had to be her decision. However, she felt that the doctors did not explain sufficiently nor spend time with her. There was no automatic referral to a social worker either before or after surgery. When I saw her she seemed stunned at the loss of her limb. Apparently, at no time had she had opportunity to discuss this with anyone who could assist her to adjust to her loss.'

Several people lacked knowledge about the purpose of medication which they were taking. An elderly person who had been at home for two weeks said:

> 'I was given lots of medicine and tablets when I was discharged but I was not told what they were for. I was just given the name and the label. I still do not know what these tablets are for except I do know which are the sleeping pills. It would be nice if people took the time to explain things a lot more when you are in hospital'.

The experience of confusion and of 'not knowing where I was' was mentioned by some people in relation both to waking up in the ward on the first morning (especially after an emergency admission) and in relation to recovering from an anaesthetic. The memory of having been confused had later worried many of these elderly people, who did not realise that this experience could be the effect of an anaesthetic and that it did not mean that they were becoming irreversibly demented themselves.

> 'After the anaesthetic I woke at 2.30 a.m. I did not know where I was, I was totally confused. Someone should have explained that shouldn't they? I was very sick. My head went up and down and I felt very frightened'.

Visitors

Whether or not elderly people in the sample were visited whilst they were in hospital and by whom was an early indication of their isolation in the community and hence their potential vulnerability after discharge. Most of this sample of elderly people were visited regularly while they were in hospital by their relatives or friends. However, fourteen people (20% of the sample) were seldom visited or visited only by people with whom they had relatively casual contact such as neighbours. In three of these cases the home help was the only visitor; the head of the day centre was the only person to visit another old person.

> 'I've not got nobody—nobody in the world. My home help was the only person to come to see me. I've got a nephew living alive somewhere—but he wouldn't know if I was alive or dead'.

Preparation for discharge

Elderly people were asked a series of questions about events which had led up to their discharge. Some of these questions and the replies to them are reproduced here. It must be emphasised that these questions were about events which had happened two or more weeks earlier and that the people interviewed were at least 75 years of age. However, the clarity and vehemence of many replies indicated that they represented a reasonably accurate account of the memories of recent discharge experience.

Feelings of recovery

'Compared with how you felt in yourself when you went into hospital, did you feel better or worse when you came out?'

The immediate effect of being in hospital is not necessarily a feeling of recovery. One third of the sample described feeling better or almost recovered, but thirty six people (52%) said that although their illness had been treated they still felt weak or ill on discharge. Seven people faced either a new or a continuing physical challenge on their discharge because, for example, they had been given a colostomy, had had an amputation or were adjusting to the effects of a stroke.

'How are you feeling now' (i.e. on the day of interview)?

The answers to this question described a similar pattern in the present as there had been in the recent past. One quarter said they felt well or reasonably well, a half indicated they felt fairly well or 'so so' and a quarter described feeling ill or 'not well'. There was little difference in how people said they felt in relation to whether they had experienced a planned or unplanned admission to hospital, or whether they had had surgery as Table 7.4 shows.

**Table 7.4
Elderly People Two
Weeks After
Discharge:
Whether Treatment
Included Surgery
and How the
Elderly Person was
'Feeling Now'
(N=69*)**

How EP was 'feeling now'	Treatment included surgery?	
	Yes (26)	No (40)
	%	%
Well/reasonably well	42	15
Fairly well/so-so	35	58
Not well/ill	23	27

*   Includes 3 cases for which surgery was not recorded.

Timing of Discharge

'Was your discharge from hospital at about the time you expected'?

Only one in five people said they had been discharged from hospital earlier than they had expected, a quarter were discharged at the time they expected and for a fifth their discharge was delayed beyond the expected date. Other replies were unreliable.

'Did you feel ready for discharge from hospital'?

This has been found to be an important question in other research studies. Like studies which had been conducted in Liverpool (NCCOP, 1978a) and Wales (Victor, nd), the elderly people in this sample were asked whether they had felt their discharge was 'too soon' (they were not ready), that it was 'about right' or that it was 'not soon enough'

One quarter (24%) of the elderly people we interviewed felt they had been discharged 'too soon' compared with 15% in Liverpool and 10% in Wales. In Brighton, 19% of patients expressed reluctance to leave hospital (Williamson, 1985). In most of the latter cases this was either because they were worried about having no-one at home to help them, or because they had inconvenient accommodation or they felt that they needed more medical treatment. Patients who had been admitted following falls or accidents or who had undergone surgery or hip replacements were also found in the Brighton study to express particular apprehension about the prospect of their discharge.

Recall of Discharge Planning

'Had you talked to anybody in hospital about how you would manage when you came home'?

Two thirds of people in our sample reported discussions with hospital staff prior to discharge but a third (35%) had not had such discussion. There is some variation between other research studies in the proportion of patients who said they had had an opportunity to discuss their anxieties and potential need for help after discharge. In Brighton and in the CCP study in Liverpool half the elderly people said they had not had a chance for such discussion. The most favourable picture was reported in Wales where, as in our sample, only one third of patients said they had lacked an opportunity to discuss how they would manage on their return home (Victor, nd). Patients in the older age groups and those from the geriatric hospital in Wales most often said that these matters had been discussed with them.

'Trial' visits home in the company of an occupational therapist were arranged for twelve people in our sample. All except one of these people had been in hospital for at least one month.

'As far as you know was there any disagreement between people about you coming out of hospital or the services you should have'?

Open disagreements about discharge were reported by only nine people and were for various reasons. For example, permanent residential care was being suggested by relatives to three of the elderly people who were interviewed and was being resisted by all three. Three other people had decided the date of their own discharge (one after reading her medical notes) and had insisted upon agreement from the medical staff.

'Was anybody worried about your discharge?'

This question produced some sad replies from a minority of elderly people which reflected their care network—or lack of it. Although two thirds said nobody had seemed worried about their discharge this reply had different meanings. Those who were in close contact with their relatives or friends either reported that other people were worried about them because this was evidence of their concern and affection or else they said their relatives were not worried because all arrangements for discharge had been made. A minority of elderly people said nobody was worried because they had no close relatives or friends who cared enough about them to be so concerned.

'How much notice were you given that you would be coming home from hospital'?

Length of notice of discharge is obviously important for several reasons. Adequate notice gives the elderly person and their carer an opportunity to prepare themselves and it allows providers of community care services time to assess and plan appropriate service cover. However, pressure on hospital beds and the cost of hospital care means that discharge will be sought as soon as the patient is deemed to have completed medical treatment.

Three fifths of the people interviewed said that they had been given more than one day's notice of their discharge. One in four had been notified the day before discharge. Only eight people (13%) were notified on the day that discharge was due to take place. Table 7.5 shows that people who had been in hospital longer received more notice of their discharge. Comparison with the previous chapter shows that the notice of discharge given to home help organisers was, on average, considerably shorter than the notice of discharge reported by elderly people.

Table 7.5
Elderly People Two Weeks After Discharge: Timing of Notice of Discharge and Length of Stay in Hospital (N=69*)

Timing of notice of discharge	Length of stay in hospital		
	1 week or less (15)	More than 1 week (42)*	Not known (12)
	N	N	N
Same day/day before	11	12	3
More than a day before	4	26	9

* Includes 4 cases where length of notice was not recorded.

There has been much discussion in the literature and in other research studies about the impact of short notice of discharge from hospital. Most studies conclude that, especially for the elderly living alone, one or two days notice of discharge did not give adequate time for services to be arranged. Although proportions differ, all studies found that a large minority of elderly people were receiving an unacceptably short notice of discharge.

Under 24 hours notice (which included those notified on the same day as discharge) was given to 56% of discharged patients in the CCP study in Birmingham in 1978 (NCCOP, 1978a), to 39% of patients studied in Wales in 1981 (Victor, nd) and to 35% of patients in Brighton in 1984 (Williamson,1985). Various studies report that patients with shorter stays in hospital are more likely to be given short notice of discharge. Our findings are in line with this.

Most of the elderly people in our sample had clearly been longing for their discharge from hospital and could not get home quick enough, however short the notice they were given. There was little relationship between notice of discharge and how they said they were feeling.

Somewhat unexpectedly, we found that saying 'goodbye' was important for a minority of people, especially those who were not accompanied by family or friends when they left hospital. Relationships with other patients on the ward and with nurses were very important to some elderly people and attention needed to be given to saying goodbye appropriately. The social need for patients to say goodbye may be difficult for hospital professionals to recognise because they see so many patients coming and going.

For example, one old lady had spent many months in hospital for treatment which included extensive surgery and she was being discharged home in a wheelchair. She was offered a home visit with an occupational therapist and was surprised to be told on her way out of the ward 'if you manage alright, we'll leave you there'.

The ward sister had said that the bed was needed—but also that she could be readmitted if things 'did not work out'. This patient's friend and her sister had prepared everything for her at home but they themselves went home about 5.00 p.m. leaving her on her own. The evening was a miserable experience for her although she had long been looking forward to her discharge home. Two weeks later the old lady was still feeling shocked and somewhat depressed by this experience and said to the interviewer:

> 'The worst part was not having the chance to go back to the hospital and stay that night in order to say goodbye to the staff and the patients I got to know so well. Looking back I know it was the right time to leave hospital, but at the time I felt thrown out'.

Hospital discharge schemes and mainstream services

Table 7.6
Type of Admission to Hospital, and Referral to Hospital Discharge Scheme/ Mainstream Service (N=69)

Type of admission	Referral to Hospital discharge scheme (40)	Mainstream service (29)	Total (69)	
	%	%	N	%
Planned	32	41	25	36
Unplanned	58	59	40	58
Other/no record	10	–	4	6

There was little difference in the referrals made to schemes or mainstream services in relation to whether the patient's admission to hospital had been planned or arose from an emergency. The differences between the two groups at discharge did not relate to the characteristics of patients but to differences in discharge procedures, especially in authorities where organisers were in close contact with ward staff through hospital discharge schemes.

Summary in the context of community care

People with cognitive loss were included in the sample which were interviewed and most were able to give some information about themselves and their experiences of hospitalisation and discharge.

Most elderly people in the sample had not been admitted to hospital from a waiting list. The possible repercussions of these unplanned admissions at the time of discharge might have been foreseen if the importance of information about types of hospital admissions had been recognised.

Three quarters of the elderly people in the sample had been in hospital for longer than one week and one in three had experienced surgery. Lack of information about the repercussions of their treatments and the purposes of the medication prescribed at discharge was one of the main complaints of the elderly people about their hospital experiences. Lack of information accentuated the loss of autonomy which had also distressed them. As most of these elderly people usually lived alone it was necessary for them to be in charge of their medication after their discharge.

One in three of the people in the sample said they had not been asked how they would manage at home after their discharge. Two fifths were told about their discharge either the day before or on the day it was due to happen. Nevertheless most people were delighted to be discharged, however precipitous the decision.

It might have been possible to predict some of those who would be vulnerable after discharge. Three key indicators of vulnerability suggested by the research are:

- unplanned admission to hospital
- usually lives alone
- seldom or never had visitors whilst in hospital

One in five elderly people were seldom or never visited whilst they were in hospital.

Elderly people in the sample had most appreciated hospitalisation for the friendships made with other patients, the kindness of the nurses, the good food and the skill of the doctors. The importance to them of these relationships with other patients and with nurses increased the distress caused by sudden discharge which removed opportunities for saying adequate 'goodbyes'.

Chapter 8

Elderly people's views of the day of discharge

Department of Health guidelines

The booklet *Discharge of Patients from Hospital* published by the Department of Health in 1989 specifies, in detail, desirable discharge procedures. Included in these are guidance on:

> *transport* .... 'ensure that suitable transport arrangements have been made' .... (para. C5);

> *access indoors* .... 'ensure ---- safe access to stairs and toilet and that it will be possible (for services) to gain entry' (para. C11);

> *arriving home* .... 'the ambulance service is responsible for informing staff on the ward from which the patient was discharged if there is no-one at home to receive a patient whom they have been told should not be left in the house alone' (para H4);

> *preparing patient's homes* .... 'ensure that for frail, disabled or elderly patients living alone arrangements have been made for their home to be heated and for food to be provided' (para. C11).

Prior to the publication of this booklet research studies over many years had identified the importance of several aspects of the first 48 hours after discharge, especially when the patient lived alone, was frail or ill and requiring continued care in the community.

Findings in relation to the Department of Health guidelines

This research was not designed specifically to test these guidelines, but it is possible to relate many of the findings of this feasibility study to particular guidelines.

Transport home from hospital

The period of the research coincided with a strike within the ambulance service. This meant that problems over transporting people home were perhaps not typical. However, discussion with home help organisers revealed that some difficulties with transport were often a feature of discharge during times not affected by a strike.

Twenty five people (36% of the sample) were brought home by an ambulance despite the strike. Two fifths were taken home in the private cars of relatives or friends which meant they were accompanied on the journey and sometimes also had other relatives or friends who were waiting for them at home. Seventeen people were brought home by the Hospital Car service. Over half the people in the sample either had no close friends or relatives or else their carers did not have cars.

Similar proportions of patients using these two main methods of transport home were also found in other studies. In the CCP (NCCOP, 1978a) study, 37% of patients went home by ambulance as did 44% in Brighton (Williamson, 1985). Relatives and friends used their own cars to bring home 40% of patients in the CCP study and 37% in Brighton.

Those patients who went home by ambulance often had to wait several hours for the ambulance to arrive. It was not unusual for people awaiting ambulances to be ready for discharge at 8.00 a.m. and to wait for between 4–10 hours in a chair somewhere in the ward for the ambulance. They were seldom told about the possibility of such delay and were therefore deprived of the choice of making alternative arrangements.

For example, three ambulances never did arrive and so the elderly people called a taxi. Many of the people who waited for transport had been in hospital for several weeks and were still feeling weak and in pain or discomfort. Two people were accompanied in the ambulance by an occupational therapist, but the rest made the journey alone.

Delays in transport had led to the assumption by some home helps, neighbours and friends that as the elderly person had not arrived home by late afternoon or evening the decision about their discharge had been changed. Unless they had been entrusted with a key home helps could not gain access until the elderly person was at home; some had called several times on the day of discharge (in unpaid time) without gaining access.

Of the people who were taken home by the hospital car service, three were accompanied by a nurse, occupational therapist and social worker respectively, but the rest were alone. The car drivers left four of these unaccompanied people at their front doors with their luggage; in only one case did the driver carry the elderly person's luggage into her home and turn on the lights.

Access indoors

Some relatives used their cars to transport patients home, in order to off-set the effects of the ambulance strike and to avoid delays, but this was an inappropriate course of action for some elderly relatives who lacked the strength to support a weak patient in and out of a car.

The reality of the ambulance strike appears to have been largely ignored by hospital personnel. Getting from hospital to home involved more than the type of transport used. The patient had to get from the door of the hospital into a car and more importantly, had to be able to get into their home at the journey's end. Some elderly people lived in upstairs flats, but when discharged from hospital some either could not climb stairs at all or could only do so with considerable support from others. The need to borrow a wheelchair from the hospital to transport a patient to a car indicated their immobility, but it seemed questions were never asked about how they would manage at the end of the journey. The elderly husband, sister and son of three patients were still suffering from strained muscles three months later which had been caused by carrying immobile old people upstairs on the day of discharge. Tragically, another elderly husband who was himself weak and ill with a heart condition supported his wife upstairs and himself died suddenly the next day as an apparent consequence.

Apart from the ambulance strike, it seemed there was no clear understanding about who was responsible for the quality of transfer between hospital and home. It seems reasonable that hospitals should be responsible for ensuring that people are transported back to their own homes without danger to themselves or damage to others.

It also seems reasonable to expect that ward staff should know whether the patient has to negotiate steps to their front door and should assess the degree of help he or she will require to climb these. This information, together with awareness of the age and physical state of the car driver, should provide guidance about whether additional help should be obtained for the patient's journey home.

Arriving home

The strongest determining influence on the quality of their discharge and on their enjoyment of being discharged from hospital was whether or not patients had relatives or friends who rallied to help. Two fifths of the sample had relatives or friends who turned discharge into a celebration. Over half the people in the sample were not in this fortunate position. Two fifths of the sample had somebody waiting for them at home; in five of these twenty six cases this person was a home help who had been given a key in order to prepare the home for the elderly person's arrival.

Table 8.1 shows that nearly all patients (65%) had somebody, (a relative, friend or neighbour) who called in to see them on the day of their discharge. In most cases (48% of the sample) these visits were relatively brief. Such contacts varied from a neighbour who called in for five minutes, to neighbours who spent most of the afternoon or evening helping an old person to settle in. In five cases home helps were at home to greet the elderly person, and in five more cases home helps called in on the day of discharge.

Table 8.1
Whether Some-one
Stayed at Home*
with the Elderly
Person on Day of
Discharge (N=69)

	%
Yes—some-one all day	17
Yes—some-one for short time	48
No	15
Not applicable/not known	20
(went to relations or nursing home/lives with others)	

* Includes 'called in'.

Preparing patients' homes and the arrival of services

Although most people in the sample had help to prepare their homes after discharge there were a minority who had little or no assistance. Twelve people (17% of the sample) arrived home alone and were alone for the rest of the day. Most had had some food left for them by neighbours or relatives, but this could be an inadequate substitute for personal help. For these twelve people and for others who had only brief visits after their arrival, their discharge could be a dreary experience. For example, a lady who was confined to a wheelchair in an upstairs flat said *'my neighbour had brought me in some food, but had forgotten the milk'*. The next visitor this lady had was her home help three days later.

This situation reflects the findings of other studies. One in five of the elderly patients discharged from hospital in Birmingham in 1978 (NCCOP, 1978a), and in Brighton in 1985 (Williamson, 1985) had arrived home to an empty house.

As we showed in chapter 7, the admission to hospital of most of the elderly people in the sample had been unplanned and most lived alone. Those who did not have family or friends to care for their homes whilst they were away therefore returned to the repercussions of their emergency admissions. Unheated rooms, food which had gone bad, dead house plants and dust were mentioned by several people who found themselves in these situations. As these elderly people were disabled and frail when they were discharged and were unable to go out on their own, their situations could have been more serious if it had been winter or if neighbours and home helps had not provided help quickly.

Organisers said that assumptions had sometimes been made by ward staff about care networks which proved to be mistaken. For example, one lady was known to have a group of caring neighbours, but nobody had found out that these neighbours had booked a day trip away together on the day of her discharge. Because another lady lived in warden-controlled sheltered housing, it was assumed the warden would cope with her needs on discharge. In fact, the warden had not been informed of this lady's pending arrival and had gone away for the weekend.

By contrast, one quarter of patients in the sample had relatives or friends who remained during the days immediately after their discharge. Some went to stay with relatives for a weekend or for one or two weeks, others had relatives who had made special arrangements to stay in the elderly person's home during the period they settled in. Some relatives had taken special leave from their jobs or had travelled long distances in order to do this.

For three fifths of the sample home help from either a discharge scheme or a mainstream service was provided either on the day of discharge or on the day following discharge.

Good and bad discharges

The interaction of discharge procedures can be compounded into a good or bad discharge. In order to get an overview of discharge procedures and practices a score was given to the presence of five components of 'good' discharge. These were whether a patient:

- was given at least 24 hours notice of discharge
- was given an opportunity to discuss how they would manage after discharge
- had somebody with them on the journey home
- had somebody waiting for them at home
- had somebody who called to see them on the day of discharge.

This score was then compared with other factors relating to hospitalisation and discharge.

Table 8.2 Elderly People Two Weeks After Discharge: Average Number of Five 'Good Discharge' Procedures and Length of Stay in Hospital (N=69*)

Length of stay in hospital (nights)	(N)	Average number of 'good discharge' procedures
1–7	(15)	2.3
8–30	(22)	2.7
31–365	(20)	3.2

* Includes 12 cases for which length of stay was not recorded.

Table 8.2 suggests that patients in the sample who had been in hospital longest experienced better discharges than did people who had been in hospital for one week or less. People who had been in hospital for longer than one week had more often talked to somebody on the ward about how they would manage after their discharge and they more often received more than 24 hours notice of discharge. However, they were not more likely to be accompanied on the journey home, nor to have somebody waiting for them on arrival. They were slightly less likely to have somebody to call to see them on the day of their discharge. Men in the sample had experienced far worse discharge procedures than women according to the score we constructed. The reasons for this are not obvious.

Table 8.3 shows that those who were discharged through the hospital discharge schemes scored more highly on the five 'good' discharge procedures. This may reflect the closer liaison between hospital discharge schemes' organisers and ward staff and the ability of organisers to visit patients on the ward soon after a referral was received. In doing so it was easier for organisers to seek permission from patients to gain access to their home prior to discharge so that could be cleaned, heated and prepared for their arrival.

Table 8.3 Elderly People Two Weeks After Discharge: Number of 'Good Discharge' Procedures and Referral to Hospital Discharge Scheme/ Mainstream Service (N=69)

Number of 'good' discharge procedures	Referral to Hospital discharge scheme (40)	Mainstream service (29)	Total (69)
	%	%	%
0–2	30	38	33
3	25	45	33
4–5	45	17	33

Cumulative effects of poor discharge practices

Two weeks after discharge one third of those who had had somebody with them on the day of their discharge said they now felt well. Nearly a half of those who did not have a visitor on the day of discharge said they felt ill or 'not well' two weeks later. The implication is not that there is a causal effect between being visited and feeling ill two weeks later. It highlights the accumulated dilemmas of those people who most often felt ill after hospitalisation, had had unplanned and brief hospital admissions, and were less often visited for an extended period on their discharge day.

Breakdown in one aspect of a discharge system, such as transport, could have painful repercussions. For example, a frail and arthritic woman was discharged home to the care of her ill husband who was himself an amputee. When asked to describe the day of his wife's discharge he said:

'She did not get here until 6.00p.m. She had been sitting in a chair in the ward since breakfast (waiting for the ambulance) so she'd stiffened right up. I managed to get her indoors but I couldn't get her into bed—so we sat in our chairs that night'.

Example of good discharge

Examples of good discharge practice amongst the sample arose especially, but not always, amongst elderly people who had been referred to a hospital discharge scheme. For example, a very frail lady in her late 80's was confined to a wheelchair after an amputation of both legs; she was determined to return home. Although medical staff doubted if this was possible, they thought she should be given a chance to manage alone.

Her discharge was handled in stages:

- She was taken home for an afternoon accompanied by an occupational therapist and the hospital discharge scheme organiser.

- During the next two weeks appropriate aids and adaptations were installed in her flat. Health and domiciliary services were planned and synchronised to cover key tasks and times and to dovetail with help from relatives.

- This elderly person returned to her home for three days. During this period she experienced the care network which had been planned.

- The effectiveness of the network was reviewed; the opinions of the elderly person, her relatives, her community nurse and home help were shared. Her general practitioner was personally involved and supportive.

- Minor alterations were made, such as moving the fridge so that she could get round it in her wheelchair and reach the food inside. She was provided with a pole to draw her curtains.

- The elderly person returned home. Three months after her discharge from hospital she was still living alone in her own home.

This one example shows that good hospital discharge practice is clearly expensive of professional time and resources but in this case it enabled the successful discharge of a very disabled and wheelchair-bound patient who would otherwise have required care in a residential home.

Example of bad discharge

Co-incidentally, the sample included another lady who had had a leg amputated, who was confined to a wheelchair and lived alone.

This person had a poor discharge experience. A trial home visit had been planned but was cancelled because the ambulance did not arrive. The following day she was discharged home without a trial visit as her hospital bed was needed. This lady lived in a flat which was jointly owned by the local authority and a housing association which had been supposedly adapted for disabled people. Conflict between the two owners over who should pay for further adaptations was unresolved.

Two weeks after discharge she was found to be in pain, and depressed. She was unable to reach her kitchen cupboards at all and struggled to reach her taps from her wheelchair because the sink needed adjusting. She had to reach over her cooker to the controls which were on a panel at the back. Her bed was too high and her armchair too low. She badly needed help to get in and out of bed.

This person had no relatives, some contact with neighbours but no regular help at weekends during which time her commode was unemptied. Her mainstream home help sometimes called, in unpaid time during the weekend, to empty the commode.

Summary in the context of community care

About one in five people had very poor discharge experiences. They needed help to prepare their homes for their arrival, especially if their admission to hospital had been unplanned. They also required far more practical help than they received after they arrived home, especially if they lived alone.

Nearly half the people in the sample relied, at discharge, on help from the statutory health and social services and relatively brief visits from neighbours and relatives.

Two fifths of the people in the sample had relatives or friends who helped them on the day of their discharge from hospital to turn their discharge into a celebration.

Waiting for transport home had been an exhausting experience for a minority of people who were interviewed. 'Transport' appeared to relate to the journey from hospital to the elderly person's front door. It was unclear who was responsible for assisting these elderly people into their homes, and perhaps up steps. Some unaided relatives or friends were unable to do this without physical strain to themselves as well as to the elderly person.

Five criteria for 'good' discharge procedure are suggested. These are that the elderly person:

- is given at least 24 hours notice of discharge
- is given an opportunity to discuss how they would manage after discharge
- has somebody with them on the journey home
- has somebody waiting for them at home
- had somebody who calls to see them on the day of discharge.

Using these criteria, one in three of the people in the sample experienced a 'good' discharge. People referred to hospital discharge schemes experienced better discharges than those referred to mainstream home help services.

Chapter 9

Elderly people's views of their abilities and difficulties two weeks after discharge

It will be recalled that when this sample of elderly people were asked how they were feeling in themselves on the day of the interview, only a quarter described feeling well, or reasonably well, nearly a half felt fairly well or 'so-so' and a quarter described not feeling well or feeling ill.

However, during interviews most of these people revealed the strength of their motivation towards recovery. Because services are mainly designed to provide assistance with difficulties, there was need to understand the self-care and other difficulties of these elderly people and the contexts in which these difficulties occurred. Although they responded to questions in interviews which were focussed on difficulties, many people conveyed the impression that their pain and physical disabilities were important primarily because they restricted the range of their social contacts and hence the quality of their lives. The repercussions of illness, such as becoming housebound, even temporarily, were vitally important for some people because of the adverse effects on their enjoyment of life.

Accommodation and self-care difficulty

The determination of the elderly people in this sample to remain permanently in their own homes was reflected in their tendency to overlook some of the ways in which their accommodation was inconvenient.

Nearly all (90%) of the sample maintained that their accommodation was either quite suitable (69%) or that it was fairly suitable (21%). Three quarters of the elderly people said their accommodation was free from damp, was not draughty and that they had warm kitchens, living rooms and bedrooms. Fewer, just over half, said they had warm WC's.

Most (70%) of the people in the sample lived in accommodation which had stairs somewhere. Two fifths of the sample had stairs inside and half had outside steps from their front door to the street. These groups included one fifth of the total sample with stairs or steps both inside and outside their homes. Four fifths of those who had any stairs were unable to climb them or could do so only with difficulty.

Less than half the sample lived in accommodation which they said was conveniently situated for the shops, the post office or public transport. Steps or stairs which they could not manage, the inconvenient location of the accommodation and lack of mobility following hospitalisation increased the struggles of the housebound.

Although we were able to interview only 28 carers, their responses showed that they had less optimistic views about the accommodation in which these elderly people lived. Carers who were relatives or friends thought that two thirds of these elderly people were living in accommodation which was either unsuitable or was detrimental to their health and safety. Only one in three were considered by their carers to be living in accommodation which was suitable to their current needs. Carers described their attempts to remedy these situations. Three had obtained sheltered flats nearer to their own homes, but the elderly people had changed their minds about moving. Other carers pointed out that the elderly person's accommodation was now too large for them and that although ways of heating it were in place, the heating was not turned on as the elderly person was apprehensive about incurring large bills. It was suspected that some elderly people were turning their heating on just before their home helps arrived. The three people who had moved into sheltered accommodation were full of praise for the comfort of their flat or bungalow and for the care they received from the warden.

Self-care abilities

As stated earlier, most (88%) of the people in this sample lived alone and therefore depended upon help from outside their household with the self-care tasks they could not manage.

The use of the Guttman scale to rate degrees of disability has been described in chapter 5. From this scale, 59% of this sample would be classified as very severely disabled, 28% as severely disabled, 6% as moderately disabled and only 7% as slightly or not disabled (Table 9.1). There was a reasonable degree of congruence in the Guttman scale scores for disability between the reports of each elderly person, their carer and the home help organiser who was responsible for planning services on their discharge.

Questions were also asked about eighteen self-care and mobility activities which presented a more detailed picture of disability. Comparison of the Guttman rating of disability with these eighteen difficulties (Table 9.1) shows that people who reported

**Table 9.1
Elderly People Two
Weeks After
Discharge: Number
of Self Care
Difficulties* and
Guttman Rating of
Disability (N=69)**

Guttman rating of disability	Number of self care difficulties			Total	
	0–6 (23)	7–11 (23)	12–18 (23)		
	%	%	%	N	%
None/slight moderate	30	9	–	9	13
Severe	52	30	–	19	28
Very severe	17	61	100	41	59

* Tasks with which elderly person had difficulty or was unable to do alone.

twelve or more difficulties were all described as 'very severely disabled' when the Guttman rating was used. There was an apparent discrepancy in those people who reported up to six of the eighteen difficulties in mobility and self care. Over two thirds of this group were also classified as severely or very severely disabled when the Guttman rating was used. This was because the Guttman rating consisted of only six of the eighteen difficulties and these were weighted.

In response to all except three of the eighteen activities listed in Table 9.2, most elderly people said that they were able to do the task with difficulty, rather than they could not manage it at all. The overall picture was one of struggle which most of the sample had in their daily lives two weeks after their discharge from hospital. The three activities which most could not do at all were their own shopping which four fifths could not manage, walking down the road unaided which three quarters were unable to do, and cutting their own toenails which two thirds could not do. This meant that three quarters of these elderly people were housebound after their discharge from hospital, unless they had a supporting arm or were taken out in a wheelchair or car.

Other tasks which required mobility and bending were also either difficult or could not be managed. Foremost amongst these was climbing stairs, which four fifths found difficult or impossible. Two thirds could not prepare meals, have a bath, shower or all-over wash or do light housework without difficulty. Nearly half described difficulty in getting in and out of bed, dressing and undressing themselves, putting on their shoes, standing by themselves or moving around their home.

In order to understand the accumulated impact of these self-care difficulties it was necessary to see the relationship of each of the eighteen difficulties with the others. Each of the eighteen difficulties was compared to the mean number of these eighteen self-care difficulties.

Multiple self-care difficulties were most often experienced by people who either were unable or had difficulty with standing unaided, dressing and undressing, making a cup of tea, eating

**Table 9.2
Elderly People's
Self Care Abilities
Two Weeks After
Discharge:
Percentage
Distribution
(N=69*)**

Tasks		Unable/ needs help	Alone with difficulty	Alone no difficulty
Shop	%	84	4	12
Walk down road	%	74	13	13
Cut own toe-nails	%	69	13	18
Climb up/down stairs/steps	%	41	41	18
Prepare meals	%	39	30	30
Light housework	%	38	29	33
Bath/shower/wash all over	%	35	36	29
Put on shoes	%	12	36	52
Stand	%	10	37	53
Make cup of tea	%	7	12	81
Hold a pen	%	4	13	83
Eat/drink	%	4	9	87
Dress/undress	%	4	42	54
Get around the house	%	3	46	51
Turn taps	%	3	12	85
Wash/shave	%	2	35	63
Get in/out of bed	%	–	43	57
Comb hair	%	–	25	75

* Percentages exclude missing records which amounted to 1 case for 6 tasks; 2 cases for 1 task; and 6 cases for 1 task. Records were complete for the remaining 10 tasks.

unaided, putting on their shoes, washing themselves, combing their own hair or holding a pen.

Conversely, people who were able to do their own shopping had, on average, only this one self care activity which was difficult or which could not be managed. Similarly, those people who were able to walk down the road unaided or who could cut their own toe-nails without difficulty had, on average, only 2.1 and 2.7 tasks respectively which they could not do or which they found difficult.

Self care difficulty and social characteristics

In this sample self care difficulties were not related to increasing age; in fact the eight people who were over ninety seemed slightly less disabled than those between seventy five and eighty years old. Self care difficulties were, however, related to gender. Women were noticeably more disabled than men, as Table 9.3 shows.

Self care difficulty and sensory loss

One third of the people in the sample said their sight was poor and another two fifths said that their sight was 'fair'. Two thirds described some loss of hearing. Table 9.4 shows that poor vision was associated with a higher number of self-care tasks which the

Table 9.3
Elderly People Two Weeks After Discharge: Gender and Guttman Rating of Disability (N=69)

Guttman rating of disability	Gender Male (17)	Female (52)	Total (69)	
	%	%	N	%
None/slight moderate/severe	59	35	28	41
Very severe	41	65	41	59
Average number of eighteen difficulties	6.9	9.7	9.0	

elderly person found difficult or impossible to manage unaided. The one blind person had fewer self-care difficulties than did those with poor vision.

Previous research on applicants for residential care (Neill *et al.*, 1988.) showed that partially sighted elderly people were often less well-provided with aids and adaptations and other types of assistance than those who were totally blind. Awareness by carers and service providers of the repercussions of an elderly person's deteriorating vision could be slow, especially if the elderly person was masking this difficulty.

In this sample poor vision was associated with age and was reported more frequently by people aged eighty five years or older. Perhaps coincidentally, the small number of men in the sample more often reported deteriorating vision.

Table 9.4
Elderly People Two Weeks After Discharge: Average Number of Self Care Difficulties* and Sight (N=69)

Elderly Person's sight		Average number of eighteen self care difficulties
	N	
Very good	(11)	7.0
Fairly good	(31)	8.4
Poor	(26)	10.7
Blind	(1)	4.0

* 18 tasks with which elderly person had difficulty or was unable to do alone.

There was congruence between the difficulties in self-care, mobility and sight reported by elderly people and the opinions of their carers. Carers were less often aware of the elderly person's reported difficulties in climbing stairs, combing their hair, turning a tap or holding a pen, but variations were small and could be co-incidental.

Pain

In response to two separate questions about pain, over two thirds of these elderly people said they experienced some degree of pain. One fifth described their pain as continuous and severe and one quarter said their pain was severe but episodic. A further quarter said they either had occasional, moderate pain (12%) or mild aches and pains (15%). Table 9.5 shows that one third of the sample were both very severely disabled and said they experienced severe pain.

When asked whether their pain had been medically assessed, four fifths (84%) of those in severe pain and two thirds (72%) of those who described their pain as moderate or mild said this had been medically assessed.

Although the same proportion of men and women reported the presence of pain, women more often described their pain as severe. More men said their pain was moderate or mild. However, it will be recalled that men were less disabled in other ways.

Table 9.5 Elderly People Two Weeks After Discharge: Pain and Guttman Rating of Disability (N=69)

Guttman rating of disability	Pain None (18)	Mild/moderate (18)	Severe (31)	Total (69)*	
	N	N	N	N	%
None/slight/ moderate	5	2	2	9	13
Severe	5	6	6	17	25
Very Severe	8	10	23	41	61
Average number of 18 self care difficulties	7.6	8.7	10.2	9.1	

* Includes 2 cases where pain was not recorded and excluded from percentages.

Daily routine

To be most effective, help from carers or services not only has to be targeted at the tasks which are difficult or impossible for an elderly person to perform, it also has to be provided at the times when these difficulties arise.

It will be recalled that nearly a half of elderly people in this sample reported difficulty with getting in and out of bed, with dressing and undressing, with standing, with putting on their shoes and with moving around the house. Most said they still felt weak or ill following their hospitalisation. For several reasons, therefore, it was important to understand these people's normal routines in a usual day. It seemed probable that they would still be trying to follow these routines, however great their struggles.

Getting up and going to bed

As a general rule what time do you like to get up? Although these elderly people had been discharged from hospital for only two weeks, two thirds liked to get up by 8.00 a.m. or earlier. Their getting up times started at 5.00 a.m. A quarter of the sample liked to be up by 7.00 a.m. and a further two fifths got up between 7.30 and 8.00 a.m. All except one person was up by 10.00 a.m.

There was a wider range of preferred times of going to bed. One third liked to go to bed between 5.00 and 9.00 p.m, but most people in the sample preferred to go to bed later than this. Nearly half went to bed between 9.00 p.m. and midnight and three people went to bed in the early hours of the morning. Services such as home help may concentrate their working hours between 9.00 a.m. and 4.00 p.m. There is, therefore, a potential mis-match between the times help may be required, with getting in and out of bed, for example, and the times services are most easily available.

Sleep, pain and 'frequency'

Elderly people were asked: *'Do you ever have problems with your waterworks (holding your water, incontinence) during the day? night? day and night?* One third said they had such problems only at night, twelve had problems only during the day and eight day and night. Therefore, two thirds of the sample had some regular problems with 'frequency' of urine.

Three quarters of the elderly people said they did not usually sleep very well and described their usual night's sleep as fair (44%) or poor (30%). Although one quarter of the sample said they slept better since coming out of hospital, 10% said they slept worse since discharge. In most cases it seemed poor sleep patterns had been unaffected by hospital admission.

Of the fifty one people who did not sleep well, eighteen, said they kept waking up, ten could not get to sleep and four woke early. Two thirds of those who slept poorly said they were in pain. Incontinence and 'frequency' was also related to sleep difficulty and applied equally to men and women. Over two fifths of those who did not sleep well had 'problems with their waterworks'— three times as many as those who said they slept well. Nearly a third of the sample took sleeping pills. This included over half of those who still slept poorly, a fifth of those who slept only 'fairly' well and a quarter of the people who slept well.

The implications of these erratic sleep patterns and nocturnal activity, amongst people who were recently hospitalised, disabled, mostly living alone, and feeling weak or 'not well' are obvious. Assessments for aids, adaptations and services often refer to the hours of daylight, but it was clear that there was a good deal of activity and struggle in the homes of these elderly people during night time hours.

Depression

The importance of their morale and quality of life was emphasised by elderly people during interviews. It was reasonable to wonder if pain, incontinence and self-care difficulties might be associated with depression or a lowering of morale. The scores, which were derived from questions developed by Bird and her colleagues, appeared to identify reliably those people who might be depressed. None of these twelve questions contained the word 'depression'. The replies of twenty five (35%) of the elderly people resulted in a morale score of 6 or higher, indicating possible depression, which needed clinical assessment.

As Table 9.6 shows, overall, depression was not related to self-care difficulty or pain but it was related to poor sleep. There were exceptions. The small group of people who had between twelve and eighteen self-care difficulties did have a higher average depression score than the rest of the sample, but numbers were small. The situations of this small minority of very disabled people, some of whom were chair-bound, might merit further study with larger numbers. One third of those with the lowest number of self care difficulties were rated as possibly depressed.

Those people who could not get to sleep had, on average, lower morale than groups experiencing other types of difficulty with sleep. Not being able to get to sleep is a recognised symptom of

**Table 9.6
Elderly People Two Weeks After Discharge: Selected Characteristics and Average Morale Score (N=69*)**

	(N)	Average**
Number of self care difficulties		
0–6	(23)	3.9
7–11	(23)	4.0
12–18	(23)	4.9
Pain		
None	(18)	3.2
Mild/moderate	(18)	3.7
Severe	(31)	5.0
Sleep		
Very well	(17)	3.2
Fairly well	(31)	4.2
Poorly	(21)	5.7
Feeling a burden		
No	(40)	3.4
Probably yes	(15)	4.3
Definitely yes	(12)	7.2
Feeling lonely		
Almost never	(24)	2.7
Sometimes	(28)	4.1
Quite often	(16)	6.7

* Row totals may exclude occasional missing records
** A score of 6 or over indicates possible depression.

clinical depression. The elderly people who felt, when asked, that they were a burden on their carers or who said they were lonely were also more likely to be depressed.

The contents of interviews of the 35% of elderly people in the sample whose scores indicated possible depression were explored to identify other reasons for this. Loneliness and fear that their physical disabilities would over-burden their carers were coupled with social isolation and losses of various types for most of these apparently depressed elderly people. Twenty one of these twenty five people lived alone and seventeen had no reliable care network. Four lived with an elderly spouse or sister and there was considerable stress on these carers, so that fear of 'being a burden' was legitimate.

One third of these depressed people had experienced various types of loss. The recent death of a spouse or other key person had been experienced by three. Six had had other types of losses of personal ability and self-image, such as major strokes, amputation or worsening Parkinson's disease. Social isolation, lack of confidence in their care network and fear of being a 'burden' on their carers seemed to be the key factors. Sadly, two thirds of these depressed people had also experienced delay, or muddle, during their discharge from hospital and the provisions of only the minimum level of services after they had arrived home.

It seemed that few people who had experienced loss of a person, of a limb or loss of the ability to control their body had been referred to a social worker or other counsellor. In general, depression and the ways available to help it was not recognised.

The quality of life of elderly people

As so many of these elderly people were severely disabled and sometimes depressed after their discharge from hospital, it was important to try to understand their feelings about the quality of their lives as they perceived them. The motivation to recover, to withstand pain and disability and the determination to retain life at home rather than in an institution stemmed from personal aims and a belief that life could be enjoyable and worth living. Their verbatim comments during interviews provided some insights into the motivations of these elderly people two weeks after their discharge from hospital.

Two thirds of the sample said they often (23%) or sometimes (40%) felt lonely. Although 'loneliness' may be regarded as an inevitable human experience, the types of loneliness conveyed by many of these people reflected their experiences of physical and emotional isolation and their apprehensions about the future. Living alone did not necessarily mean people in the sample felt lonely; living with others did not mean they were not lonely. There were different types and reasons for loneliness which were described. For example, one third of the people in the sample thought they were definitely (17%) or probably (21%) a burden on their carers. Whether or not their care was actually experienced as a 'burden' this feeling implied that a component of obligation and one-sided dependence had crept into the relationships between this small group of elderly people and their carers. The minority of carers who were interviewed confirmed this.

Research on the interaction of social and emotional factors and the ability of elderly people to cope with pain (Walker, 1991) concludes that pain cannot be assessed in isolation from other life events. Different factors which influenced ability to cope with pain were explored in Walker's research. These included regrets about the past, loneliness, financial and personal problems and religious beliefs. The importance of such a holistic research approach is in line with the impressions gained from the sample of elderly people we interviewed.

Being housebound

As mentioned earlier, three quarters of the people interviewed were unable to go out alone two weeks after their discharge. Although being housebound was not related to the score denoting possible clinical depression, the content of interviews indicated that the deprivation of social contact through enforced confinement indoors was destructive to some people . When asked, 77% of the people interviewed said they would like to be able to go out more. Replies to questions about where they would like to go and what they were looking forward to in the future illustrated the current gaps in their lives.

Ambitions were modest. The most common wishes were to go to the shops to collect their own pensions, to visit friends or to go out 'if only just for a walk round'. Sundays were mentioned by several people as a special day during which there should be a different routine. Some people wanted to be able to go to church or visit a grave or to be beside the sea, which for some was nearby.

> 'Church on Sunday and visit a friend afterward'.
> 'To visit my husband's grave'.
>
> '...... to go to the seafront, along the promenade. Find a seat, book a midday meal. Have a meal and then get a taxi home'.
>
> 'To church on Sunday. Visit a friend. To the country—a National Trust Garden'.

Some people in the sample were taken out by relatives in their cars at weekends. None of these people expressed the same degree of longing to go out as other people who did not have such regular outings. One person was being taken out by a volunteer. The encouragement she derived from this was obvious.

> 'Twice a week I walk a few steps up the street with the Age Concern lady. I'd love to go into town to visit my friends'.

It was evident that this sample of disabled elderly people had, in most cases, gained much from making new relationships during their hospitalisation. After their discharge from hospital some found themselves in a downward spiral when being housebound could increase their pre-occupation with pain and disability, diminish their feelings of self-worth and confidence and so make them increasingly dependent on others.

The researcher's impressions were that the repercussions of being housebound which the elderly people described were important. Some people who had been housebound for an extended period before and after their hospitalisation seemed to have become almost agoraphobic in their reactions. Their world had shrunk to the confines of their own homes or even to one room. When opportunity for an occasional outing arose, such as a Christmas party, they were apprehensive about going out and mixing again with other people. Such reactions appeared similar to the institutionalised reactions of people who were socially isolated in settings other than a private household. Further study might be desirable to explore ways in which becoming a long-term 'institutionalised' housebound person in a private household might be prevented.

Table 9.7
Elderly People Two Weeks After Discharge: Number of Self Care Difficulties* and Referral to Hospital Discharge Scheme/ Mainstream Service** (N=69)

Number of self care difficulties	Referral to Hospital discharge scheme (35)	Mainstream service (34)	Total (69)	
	%	%	N	%
0–6	34	32	23	33
7–11	31	35	23	33
12–18	34	32	23	33
Average number	9.1	8.8	9.0	

* Tasks which elderly person could only 'manage alone—with difficulty' or was 'unable/needed help to do'.

** Adjusted to take account of referral process in authority C.

Hospital discharge schemes and mainstream service

Overall, people in the sample who had been referred to hospital discharge schemes and to mainstream home help services were similar in their degrees of disability and in the average numbers of self care tasks which they found difficult or could not manage (Table 9.7).

However, this overall similarity masked differences within and between local authorities. The people in the sample being helped by scheme D were noticeably more disabled in terms of self-care than any other group in the sample; they were also older. It will be recalled that this organiser D filtered a large number of referrals of people discharged from several hospitals. It was clear that this organiser was retaining the most disabled people for help from her own team of workers and was passing the less disabled and younger to mainstream service organisers.

By contrast, people in the sample who had been referred to the mainstream organisers in departments A, B and C were slightly more disabled than those who had been referred to each of the discharge schemes in these authorities.

Summary in the context of community care

Nearly all the people in the sample could be described as severely disabled when they were interviewed two weeks after their discharge from hospital. Most lacked some self-care ability. Disability was not related to age in this small sample, but the women in the sample were more disabled than the men. Two thirds of the sixty nine people who were interviewed were experiencing some degree of pain, three quarters described poor sleep patterns and three fifths described some loss of bladder control. Only one in four people said they felt well; the rest qualified this reply.

Although nearly all the elderly people interviewed maintained that their accommodation was 'suitable', this was probably because they wished to remain there. However, over two thirds had steps to their front door or stairs inside their home and most could not climb these or could do so only with difficulty. Over half the sample lived in accommodation which was inconvenient for shops, the post office or public transport. Three quarters of the elderly people were housebound two weeks after their discharge from hospital.

Replies to questions about their usual daily routines revealed that most people in the sample liked to get up before 8.0 a.m and two thirds did not go to bed until after 9.0 p.m. If services, such as home help, function between 9.0 a.m–4.0 p.m they are unlikely to be appropriate for those people who require help with tasks associated with getting up or going to bed.

Poor sleep patterns, pain and 'frequency' of urine meant that many of this sample of elderly people were active at night. Nocturnal activity coupled with the poor mobility and balance of some has clear implications for the need for telephones or accessible alarm systems. One in three of the sample said they took sleeping pills, but this medication did not seem to be clearly associated with good sleep patterns.

One in three of the people in the sample were possibly clinically depressed. Depression was not related to the degree of people's physical disability, or to their experiences of pain, but it was related to social and emotional factors such as feeling lonely or fearing they were a burden on their carers. Losses of various types were also described. One in three of the least disabled people in the sample were possibly depressed. There was no indication that the possible clinical depression of a third of the elderly people in the sample had either been recognised or was being treated.

The elderly people who were interviewed complained more about the quality of their lives than about their physical disabilities or pain. Being housebound was especially difficult because this eroded social contact and stimulation and apparently reduced both their motivation towards recovery and their capacity to withstand disability and pain. Social contact with their home help became even more important. Few elderly people in the sample received services such as day care which took them out of their homes on a regular basis.

Chapter 10

Home help from hospital discharge schemes and mainstream services

In the previous chapter some of the self-care difficulties of people in the sample were described. We now consider how far the type and extent of home help given after discharge from hospital met these difficulties.

Two weeks after discharge, home helps from the hospital discharge schemes were still deployed. Mainstream home help services were also supplying those elderly people referred to them with extra hours when resources permitted. There was a policy in all four local authorities of providing an intensive service to people after their discharge from hospital, when this was possible and necessary.

Previous experience of home help

Half the sample had had a home help before their admission to hospital. Half of these (26% of the sample) had their previous home help back after discharge. Some of these seventeen people had been visited by their home help while they were in hospital. For half the sample having home help was a new experience. There were no overall differences in the proportions of 'new' cases to hospital discharge schemes and mainstream services, but there were differences within local authorities. For example, the discharge scheme in authority B was available only to people who had not had home help before their admission to hospital. If they had had a home help previously they were referred back to the mainstream home help organiser. More women than men in the sample had had a home help prior to hospitalisation.

Amount of home help provision

Anticipated provision

It will be recalled that after they had met and assessed each person in the sample the appropriate organiser was asked how much home help provision they thought would be required after discharge. These predictions were then compared with the help which was provided. In two out of three cases organisers over-estimated the hours of home help which would be given and the number of days per week the home help would visit. The predictions which proved to be correct were of the number of people for whom home help would be supplied on six or seven days weekly and that women would receive more home help than men. The latter expectation probably reflected the organisers' assessments of the greater disability of women.

Actual home help provision

After their discharge, almost a third of the elderly people in the sample received less than two hours of home help each week (Table 10.1). A further third of the sample received between two and four and a half hours of home help each week. Fourteen was the maximum number of home help hours provided and was given to two people. On average, each person in the sample received 4.0 hours home help each week.

Table 10.1 Elderly People Two Weeks After Discharge: Number of Hours and Days and Intensity of Home Help Service and Referral to Hospital Discharge Scheme/ Mainstream Service (N=69*)

Home help service	Referral to Hospital discharge scheme %	Mainstream service %	Total N	%
Number of hours	(34)	(32)	(66)	
Less than 2	15	47	20	30
2–4.5	32	37	23	35
5–14	53	16	23	35
Number of days	(35)	(32)	(67)	
1	14	44	19	28
2–4	34	41	25	37
5–7	51	16	23	34
Intensity	(34)	(31)	(65)	
Low	24	55	25	39
Medium	47	32	26	40
High	29	13	14	21

* Includes 3 missing records for hours and 2 for days.
  Low Intensity: 0–2 hours on 1–2 days.
  Medium Intensity: 2.5–6 hours on 2–5 days.
  High Intensity: 7–14 hours on 5–7 days.

A quarter (28%) of the sample received home help on only one day per week and just over a third had a home help on between two and four days each week. Whereas a third received at least five days, only a minority (16%) had visits from a home help on six or seven days weekly. This was the group which had some home help cover at the weekend. In summary, a highly intensive home help service, in terms of hours and days, was being provided to only one sixth (16%) of all the people in the sample two weeks after their discharge from hospital.

Variations in provision

Although the oldest people in the sample were not more disabled according to their own accounts, there were indications that they received home help on more days per week. If true, this meant that organisers' sympathy or admiration for great age might have sparked greater provision.

Overall, there was a clear distinction between men and women in the sample. Half the men and a fifth of the women received home help on one day per week only. Only one of the seventeen men compared with a fifth of the women had home help on five days per week, probably Monday to Friday. However, for the 16% of the sample who were receiving weekend cover there was no difference between the sexes.

There were also differences between the ways hospital discharge schemes and mainstream services allocated home help time. As Table 10.1 also shows, more intensive help was provided by the hospital discharge schemes than by the mainstream services. Half of the people referred to hospital discharge schemes were receiving home help for between five to fourteen hours per week,

Table 10.2 Elderly People Two Weeks After Discharge: Number of Hours of Home Help Service, Number of Self Care Difficulties and Referral to Hospital Discharge Scheme/ Mainstream Service (N=69*)

Number of hours service	*Referral to hospital discharge scheme* Number of self care difficulties			*Referral to mainstream service* Number of self care difficulties			Total
	0–6	7–11	12–18	0–6	7–11	12–18	
	N	N	N	N	N	N	N
Less than 2	3	2	–	8	6	1	20
2–4.5	3	6	2	3	3	6	23
5–14	5	3	10	–	3	2	23
Total N	11	11	12	11	12	9	66
Average hours	4.0	3.2	7.2	1.6	3.4	4.5	4.0

* Includes 3 cases for which information was missing and excluded from percentages.

compared with one in six of people referred to mainstream services. On average, elderly people referred to schemes received 4.9 hours; those referred to mainstream services received 3.1 hours (per week).

As Table 10.2 shows, scheme organisers targeted their home help provision to people who had most self-care difficulties; to the 'heavy' end. Mainstream services were not targeted in this way. Thus, four fifths of the people referred to discharge schemes who had between 12–18 self care difficulties received 5–14 hours' home help each week. Only one in four of the group of similarly disabled people who were referred to mainstream services received help for a comparable number of hours.

The tasks of home helps

Home help organisers, elderly people, their carers and their home helps were asked to respond to an identical list of home help tasks and in relation to each task they were asked to say whether the home help did the task 'usually/always', 'sometimes' or 'seldom/never'. As interviews with different respondents were conducted at different stages of the discharge process, we concentrate first on the statements of elderly people about the tasks performed by their home helps two weeks after they had been discharged from hospital.

The list of home help tasks had been adapted from the previous work of a colleague in the Research Unit at the National Institute for Social Work (SSI, 1990) and were considered in five sections according to the nature of the work.

1. Ten *housework* tasks (washing up, making beds, different types of cleaning).
2. Three *food* tasks (preparing and cooking food).
3. Five *outside contact* tasks (collecting prescriptions or pensions, paying bills, shopping).
4. Nine *personal care* tasks (getting into/out of bed, washing, dressing, going to WC, taking medicine/pills).
5. Eleven *social contact* tasks (sitting and talking, listening to problems, giving advice, contacting relatives, friends or the GP, taking out to shops or hospital).

Housework

It is clear from Table 10.3 that the types of help usually or sometimes given by home helps to most of the people in the sample were help with cleaning, shopping, and talking with them over a cup of tea. There was little difference between hospital discharge schemes workers and mainstream home helps in the tasks they did.

Two thirds of the sample either had difficulty with housework and cleaning tasks or else could not manage these at all. It is therefore understandable that help with housework should predominate in the roles of home helps. When asked, 83% of the

**Table 10.3
Selected Home
Help Tasks: Home
Help Organisers'
Expectations and
Elderly People's
Statements Two
Weeks After
Discharge (N=69)**

Type of home help task		Organisers' expectations** usually/ sometimes	seldom/ never	Elderly people's statements usually/ sometimes	seldom/ never
Housework					
washing up	%	80	20	49	51
make beds	%	89	11	64	36
light cleaning	%	89	11	81	19
clean surfaces	%	97	3	85	15
empty commode*	%	42	58	39	61
clean floors	%	92	8	91	9
wash floors	%	89	11	76	24
heavy cleaning	%	51	49	37	63
Food					
make drink	%	56	44	52	48
prepare food	%	41	59	13	87
cook meal	%	24	76	12	88
Outside contact					
shopping	%	68	32	61	39
collect pension	%	34	66	32	68
collect prescription	%	57	43	36	64
Personal care					
get up from bed	%	25	75	9	91
get into bed	%	5	95	4	96
dress/undress	%	26	74	7	93
wash face	%	11	89	7	93
all over wash	%	22	78	7	93
bath	%	11	89	6	94
give medicine/pills	%	11	89	4	96
Social contact					
sit and talk	%	92	8	68	32
have cup of tea	%	88	12	66	34
listen to problem	%	85	15	53	47
give advice	%	75	25	35	65
take to shops	%	20	80	9	91
contact relatives/ friends	%	56	44	25	75
contact services	%	71	29	34	66

* Percentages exclude 15 missing/not applicable cases in elderly persons' response and 14 cases in organisers' response. For all other tasks, missing records were well below 10% of cases.

** Organisers were interviewed two weeks after discharge but prior to EP interview. They were asked 'do you anticipate this home help doing any of these tasks ... now or within the 12 weeks following their discharge...?'

people interviewed said they thought that home helps did the right tasks for them.

However, there has been much discussion (Audit Commission 1985; Hedley and Norman, 1982; Parker, 1981; SSI, 1987;) about whether or not housework is an appropriate task for home helps in current and future community care. In some local authorities elderly disabled people who only require help with their housework are being regarded as ineligible for the home help service and are being referred to other private agencies who may charge fees the elderly person cannot afford. The question remains 'if the roles of home helps do not include housework, then who else should do this?'.

In a recent review of the research literature Sinclair (1990) found from a number of studies that 'neighbours do not provide ..... domestic or highly personal care for elderly people. For example, they do not wash them or clean their houses'. Furthermore, community based volunteers 'hardly figure at all in studies of the practical and personal help given to old people'. Where relatives are in contact, presumably these housework tasks fall on them, for it is clear that the disabilities of the people in the sample after their hospitalisation rendered two thirds of them incapable of doing housework themselves.

Food

Few home helps cooked meals for people in the sample. Home helps usually or sometimes made a drink for a half of these people in the sample, although four fifths were able to do this for themselves.

Outside contact

Home helps went shopping at least sometimes for nearly three fifths of these elderly people after their discharge. It will be recalled that most (88%) of the sample could not get out to do their own shopping or to collect their own pensions and prescriptions. Pensions were collected by home helps for a third of the sample, but home helps seldom, if ever, took any of the elderly people out to do these things for themselves.

Personal care

Some of the tasks carried out by home helps such as help with housework and shopping matched the difficulties being experienced by these elderly people after discharge (see Table 9.2). An apparent mismatch over the tasks done by home helps and the difficulties experienced by this sample of elderly people arises in relation to personal care functions. As Table 9.2 shows, between one third and two fifths of elderly people, on discharge, had difficulty in getting in and out of bed, dressing and undressing themselves and washing their faces. Home helps were seldom helping them with these tasks. Nearly three quarters of the people in the sample either could not, or had difficulty with having an all-over wash, shower or bath.

Social contact

One in three home helps usually, and a further third sometimes, found time to sit and talk with the elderly person over a cup of tea. Although some organisers could not 'officially' approve of the home help spending time in this way, most (92%) expected the home help to sit and talk at least sometimes. To most of the elderly people this brief personal contact was important and appreciated.

Off-duty jobs

Some home helps did jobs outside the duties for which they were paid. Such work was not illicit; in most cases organisers knew about it but were not able to sanction and pay for it officially.

These activities were explored during interviews. Two fifths of the elderly people said their home helps washed their underwear, and their bed linen. Sometimes this washing was taken home and washed in the home help's own washing machine if the elderly person did not possess a machine.

Three fifths of the home helps said they cleaned the elderly person's cooker, one third changed light bulbs, a quarter unblocked drains and cleaned brass. A clean brass knocker on their front door was very important to some elderly people. In a few cases home helps said they had enlisted help from their husbands to mend fuses, put on electric plugs and to do other minor repairs which they could not manage themselves.

Several elderly people said they wished it was possible to get 'a home help to do men's jobs'. Neglected gardens caused much anxiety to those who had them.

Hospital discharge schemes and mainstream services

It was somewhat surprising, initially, to find that the tasks performed by hospital discharge schemes home helps did not differ more markedly from the types of tasks done by mainstream home helps, especially given the greater input in terms of hours and days service provided by discharge schemes.

Further exploration of the content of interviews, however, reveals some possible reasons for the apparent lack of personal care. Schemes home helps were being provided for a pre-determined period of time to assist with rehabilitation after hospitalisation. Comments by some, but not all of the elderly people interviewed, indicated a preference for maintaining their own personal care, such as washing and dressing, if they could possibly do so despite pain and difficulty. In these situations it was the home help's role to assist when needed, but not to assume responsibility for the task, especially as he or she knew their services would be discontinued after a few weeks.

Congruence between respondents about the tasks of home helps

So far, we have presented events relating to discharge and service provision from the perspectives of elderly people themselves. The design of the research enabled comparisons to be made between the replies of the different types of respondent. As stated earlier, identical questions about the tasks of home helps were asked of organisers, elderly people, carers and home helps. The roles and functions of home helps in relation to elderly people following their discharge from hospital are of major interest and importance in the context of the current community care legislation. For this reason it is necessary to explore the extent to which the picture of services presented by elderly people in the sample is reflected in the replies of others.

Comparison between the expectations of the home help organiser and the tasks done by home helps

Two weeks after discharge organisers were asked about the tasks they expected would be necessary for each elderly person. In relation to most people, the tasks organisers expected home helps to perform were mainly housework tasks, shopping, and some provision of social contact.

Organisers anticipated that a third of the elderly people would usually need help with heavy cleaning and that it would be necessary for the home help to empty the commode for a quarter. Expectations about tasks anticipated by organisers were reflected in the tasks the home helps were reported actually to perform by the elderly people who were interviewed.

In view of the disability and recent hospitalisation of these elderly people, it was somewhat surprising that the organisers expected that few would usually require help with personal care such as getting up, getting dressed, washing themselves or with getting into or out of bed.

As described earlier, this information about home help tasks and the expectations of the organiser is derived from the responses of elderly people, their organiser and their home help, to identical lists of pre-coded questions. This provides accurate information about the tasks which were actually completed but it very probably under estimates the activities of the home helps. Although a home help may not have actually washed a person's face, it is probable that he or she might have heated the water, found the soap, flannel and towel and encouraged the elderly person to wash themselves. Similarly, food might not have been prepared, but the equipment and ingredients may have been placed in a convenient position for the elderly person to prepare their food later.

The questions we asked about the tasks of home helps were not sufficiently detailed to distinguish the different levels of help home helps provided. Similar issues have been discussed by other researchers (Stone *et al.*, 1989).

Comparisons between the views of elderly people and home helps

As home helps were only interviewed once, twelve weeks after discharge, comparison between their replies with those of the elderly people relate to these later interviews. There was a reasonable degree of congruence between what home helps said they did and what the elderly person said their home help did for them in relation to most domestic tasks. However, fewer elderly people said their home help usually washed up for them, made their beds or cleaned surfaces or floors compared with the number of home helps who claimed to do these tasks. Similar numbers of elderly people and home helps said the home help did their shopping and collected prescriptions. Even fewer elderly people than home helps said their home help assisted with personal care tasks.

It must be remembered that numbers in the sample were small, but there seemed some discrepancy between the statements of elderly people, compared to organisers and home helps, over the extent to which the home help and elderly person had social contact and particularly over the extent to which the home help listened to an elderly person's problems and gave advice. Home helps said they had sometimes sat and talked and listened to the problems of 92% of people in the sample, but only 68% of the elderly people said that this happened. Home helps thought they gave advice to three quarters of the people in the sample but only one in three elderly people said their home help had advised them.

Opinions of home helps about elderly people

Three quarters of the home helps who were interviewed said they found it easy to help elderly people in general and that they felt valued by the individual elderly person who was being discussed. Home helps were asked how they felt when they left the elderly person and they expressed a range of mixed feelings. A feeling of satisfaction was mentioned in relation to three fifths of elderly people, sadness about a quarter, resentment about a quarter and 15% made the home help feel worried when they left.

Home helps considered that one third of the elderly people in the sample had been discharged home from hospital too early. Whereas two thirds of these clients had seemed happy and confident when they come home, others had been anxious. Home helps thought that the discharge of one fifth of these elderly people could have been handled better, and that there were people available who could have done more for them. Home helps thought that one quarter of the sample were a danger to themselves at home, but they considered that such elderly people had a right to choose to live at risk.

Opinions of elderly people about home helps

As already mentioned, four fifths of the elderly people thought that their home helps did the right tasks for them and three quarters considered that they received enough home help after their discharge from hospital. Most (91%) said they felt at ease with their home help and four fifths said they could rely on their home help coming when she said she would.

Elderly people, overall, felt involved in the decision about what the home help would do on each visit. One quarter said that they and their home help would decide together what the home help would do, one fifth of elderly people said they decided themselves. One third said the home help decided and 6% said that the home help had been told by her organiser what to do.

One quarter of the elderly people thought the home help service could be improved. Some thought that a 'home help to do mens' jobs' was needed for jobs such as gardening or cleaning paintwork.

In response to questions about their home helps women revealed a different attitude to men. As mentioned earlier, more women had had a home help prior to their hospitalisation, so their greater spontaneity may arise from familiarity with the service and greater confidence to express their views about it. Women were more critical of the home help service. One third of women but no men thought the service could be improved. They also more often said they decided what tasks the home help should do on each visit, whereas the men left the home help to decide their work programme. Women also more often said they talked to their home help about their concerns and also said that the home help talked to them about her family and her worries.

Some quotations from the descriptions of elderly people and home helps about each other are given in the Appendix.

Matching home helps to elderly people

Appropriate home helps were not easily provided to a minority of elderly people who had particular needs or who were apprehensive. It was noticed that organisers took care and showed considerable skill in finding a home help who would be acceptable to an individual person. Such insight, which stemmed from their experience and their assessment of the elderly person, might not be easily achieved if assessment was completely separated from the provision of services after implementation of the NHS and Community Care Act.

For example, an elderly man who lived alone was worried after his emergency admission to hospital. He knew he had left his home in a muddle and was worried because he realised that his injuries would mean he would have to have somebody coming in to help him. When interviewed two weeks after discharge, he was completely reassured. On discharge he had been sent a male home help, whom he regarded as a 'pal' and 'a good chap'. He said his home help 'had sorted him out' including finding and re-ordering all his official papers which he thought he had long since lost.

Another elderly couple lived in an isolated rural community. The husband had been in hospital, his wife was frail and disabled and very nervous of allowing any stranger into her home. They were referred to a mainstream organiser. With perseverance and much effort this organiser managed to find a home help already known socially to this couple, who was accepted by the wife with confidence.

Differences between hospital discharge schemes and mainstream home helps

Some of the people who had help from a hospital discharge scheme had not had a home help previously and so could not make a comparison when they were first interviewed. The interviews were studied of those who had had a mainstream home help previously. Apart from having more home help hours and a wider spread of care throughout the week the most usual distinction elderly people made was that schemes' workers showed more initiative. In various ways elderly people described how schemes' workers looked for jobs which needed to be done and got on with them. This 'initiative' was described with appreciation by several people. One person said that her previous mainstream home help did not have such 'initiative'. This happened to be in the local authority where schemes and mainstream workers sometimes worked in tandem, as in this case. Interestingly, this elderly person noticed a gradual change in the behaviour of her mainstream home help who developed more 'initiative' and a more flexible attitude towards the tasks she was prepared to undertake.

Summary in the context of community care

Half of this sample of elderly people had not had a home help before their hospitalisation.

The predictions of organisers about how much home help would be provided after these patients had been discharged was accurate in only one third of the sample. Inaccuracy arose because organisers over estimated the number of home help hours which would be given. The difference between planned and actual provision, in most cases, indicated the gap between the amount of home help which was desirable and the amount which was possible.

During the two weeks after their discharge from hospital each person in the sample, on average, received 4.0 hours of home help each week.

People who were referred to a hospital discharge scheme received a more intensive home help service (average 4.9 hours per week) than those referred to mainstream services (average 3.1 hours per week). Over half of those referred to schemes had a home help on five or more days per week compared to only one in six of the elderly people referred to mainstream home help services.

Schemes organisers targeted their provision to the most disabled people referred to them. Resources of mainstream services were more sparse and distributed more evenly but attempts were also made to target severely disabled people.

In the views of some elderly people who had previous experience of a mainstream service, schemes home helps showed more initiative in identifying the tasks which needed to be done, and were more flexible in the types of work they were prepared to undertake.

The tasks most often performed by schemes and mainstream home helps were housework, shopping and providing social contact. Few helped these elderly people with personal care tasks such as getting in and out of bed, dressing and undressing or preparing meals. Although nearly all the elderly people in the sample expressed satisfaction with their home help and the types of assistance which was being provided, some thought there was a need for a 'home help to do men's jobs' such as gardening, cleaning windows and minor household maintenance.

Interviews with home helps revealed that over half were doing jobs for these elderly people outside the duties for which they were being paid. These jobs included taking washing home, clearing drains and changing light bulbs. A minority had enlisted help from their husbands with other minor repairs.

Organisers in both schemes and mainstream services emphasised the importance of 'matching' each elderly person to the 'right' home help. They were apprehensive that this process of 'matching' would be lost through the purchaser/provider split envisaged in future developments of community care. Interviews with this sample of elderly people illustrated the importance of personal affinity with their helpers.

Chapter 11

Elderly people's views of their services and care networks

By the time elderly people and their carers were interviewed two weeks after the elderly person had been discharged from hospital, their carers' responses to the 'crisis' of their discharge had died down. Relatives who had come to stay temporarily had returned to their own homes, as had elderly people who had gone to stay with relatives. The provision of home help was, in most cases, dovetailed efficiently into changes in the roles of carers during this period. To be most effective a community care service, such as home help, needs to enhance existing care networks rather than to replace them or to compete with them. After outlining our methods and the elderly people's 'roots', this chapter explores the general input of services and the composition of the care networks which were supporting these people at this point in time.

Methods

Information about care networks was obtained in three ways.
Elderly people were asked to describe:

1. – how long they had lived in their current residence and their 'roots';
   – who lived with them and the age, gender and relationship of other household members;
   – if they had relatives alive, who these relatives were, where they lived (locally, other parts of Britain, or outside the British Isles) and the nature of their contacts with the elderly person.

   Parallel questions were asked about 'other people, not relatives, who are important to you'.

2. The elderly people were asked to respond to a check-list of five weekly services and six 'less than weekly' services and say if they had the service, how often and whether they wanted more, less or the same amount of each service.

   The list of weekly services included meals on wheels, community nurse, bath aide, volunteer, home help, and day hospital or day care.

   The 'less than weekly' services included chiropodist, health visitor, social worker, general practitioner, mobile library and 'others'.

3. A grid of weekly visiting patterns of relatives, friends, neighbours, home helps and other service workers was completed for an 'average' week. Other services and visitors, such as private domestic helps and gardeners, were also recorded.

   The grid was divided into sections for each day of the week and into four time periods over each twenty four hours.

   Parallel questions were asked of the carers, who were interviewed about each elderly person's care network.

Information from (1) and (2) enabled us to indicate whether carers and services were visiting at all or if they were important to the elderly people. Not surprisingly, the most usual response from the people who were interviewed was that they were satisfied with what they had got. Typically, consumer studies in relation to elderly people have found that they tend not to complain appropriately, that they express 'gratitude' for what they are receiving and that their expectations are relatively low. In part, this may reflect a lack of general information about which services are available and about guidance on how to obtain them. The independent attitudes of some elderly people towards benefits and services may result in services being regarded as 'charity' rather than as rights. The NHS and Community Care Act tackles such issues in some detail.

As well as asking direct questions of elderly people in the sample about their service needs, a more subtle approach was also adopted through analysis of the data, by comparing the replies of different respondents to identical questions and by asking interviewers to complete an evaluation schedule. Despite all this however, shortfalls in service provision can only be matters of conjecture, because most of the elderly people themselves did not complain. The grid as in (3) above enabled us to identify the overall 'cover' of visits and to examine typical gaps in care networks.

'Roots'

It will be recalled that sixty one (88%) of the elderly people in the sample lived alone. This increased the importance of understanding the extent of their 'roots' in the local community and the nature of their local contacts.

Most of the people in the sample had lived in the same place for many years. Only one in five had lived in their present accommodation for under ten years, nearly half had lived in their current homes for between ten to twenty nine years and a third for thirty years and over. This latter group included nine people who had been resident in the same place for between fifty and eighty years.

In addition to living in the same accommodation for so long, three quarters of these people said that their 'roots' were local. 'Local' was defined as being within a fifty mile radius of their current homes. 'Roots' meant 'the place where I belong'. For some, this was where they were born, for others it was where they had spent most of their married life and brought up their children.

Relatives and friends

Most of the elderly people were part of an extended family, some of whom lived locally. All except four people said they had relatives alive and as Table 11.1 shows, three quarters had relatives living locally. On average, each elderly person in the sample had three relatives and/or friends who lived 'locally'.

Table 11.1 also shows that three fifths had friends who lived locally. This included half the sample who had both local relatives and local friends.

Eight people (12% of the sample) lived with a relative. Five lived with a spouse, two with a sister and one with her son. All these relatives defined themselves as 'carers', but it is clear that the spouses and sister were all ill or disabled themselves, sometimes more seriously so than the 'patient' identified in the sample.

Whereas some relatives were very close at hand, such as next door, over the road or in the next street, others lived further away. The ease with which they could visit the elderly person depended upon their own age and health, other responsibilities and the transport they had available.

**Table 11.1
Elderly People Two Weeks After Discharge: Relatives and Friends Living Locally***
(N=69)

	N	%
Nobody	5	7
Relatives only	17	25
Friends only	8	12
Both	34	49
No record	5	7
Total	69	100

* Within a 50 mile radius

Although most of these elderly people had lived in their current accommodation for many years they had relatively few local contacts. Two weeks after discharge, many still talked about other patients in the same ward with whom they had forged friendships during their hospitalisation. This demonstrated their ability and their wish to make new friends. Possibly the housebound existence of so many people in the sample meant that relationships which had been lost, whether through death or other reasons, were not easily renewed through new friendships. In this way the size of their informal networks had become gradually eroded.

Weekly services

Meals on wheels

As Table 11.2 shows, two weeks after discharge, meals were being delivered to a half of the sample. It will be recalled that, at this point in time, 70% of the sample had difficulty preparing their own meals.

**Table 11.2
Services Received by Elderly People Two Weeks After Discharge and Referral to Hospital Discharge Scheme/ Mainstream Service (N=69)**

Services	Referral to Hospital discharge scheme (35)*	Mainstream service (34)*	Total (69)*	
	%	%	N	%
Weekly				
meals on wheels	49	56	35	52
community nurse	38	44	28	41
bath aide	9	6	5	7
volunteer	6	–	2	3
none of above	26	24	17	25
one of above	60	50	38	55
two–four of above	14	26	14	20
Less than weekly				
chiropodist	37	38	26	38
health visitor	3	12	5	7
social worker	12	21	11	17
general practitioner	62	76	46	70
mobile library	24	18	14	21
other	14	24	13	19
none of above	11	9	7	10
one of above	51	24	26	38
two–six of above	37	68	36	52

* In most rows there were no missing records. The occasional missing record has been excluded from percentages.

People who had been in hospital for longer than one week were more likely to receive meals on wheels. Meals were also targeted at the more disabled. Three fifths of the people who experienced difficulty with more than six self-care tasks received meals compared with only two fifths of those who were less disabled. Meals were delivered as often to the small group who lived with others as they were to those who lived alone.

Most of the recipients did not receive this service at weekends. However, a few people had seven frozen meals delivered once each week. The delivery of frozen meals was an obvious advantage to those people who were unable to cook their own. But the advantage of 'surveillance' was being lost since it was clear from other cases, that often meals were being delivered not only to provide food but to ensure that someone was calling on a vulnerable elderly person. The surveillance of those housebound disabled people who did not have relatives was supplied on a day to day basis by the meals on wheels service and by neighbours.

Community nurses

Table 11.2 shows that two fifths of the sample were being visited by a community nurse two weeks after their discharge from hospital and there was no difference between schemes and mainstream services in this respect.

The community nursing service was clearly being targeted at the most disabled group. Half the twenty eight people being visited had between twelve and eighteen self-care difficulties. This meant that two thirds of the most disabled group, compared with a quarter of the least disabled group, were being visited by a community nurse.

The grids suggest that, where a nurse was in contact, she usually visited three or more times each week. Nurses visited on seven days, to treat amputations, ulcerated feet or legs, and diabetes. A stoma nurse was going to one elderly person twice a day on seven days a week.

Bath aides

Only five people were being visited by a bath aide (Table 11.2). It will be recalled that over two thirds of the sample were unable or had difficulty in having a bath, shower or all-over wash unless they had help. Although few home helps were assisting with these tasks, it seems that elderly people with these difficulties were generally being visited by community nurses. However, we cannot assume that nurses were bathing these elderly people.

Volunteers

Only two people were visited by a volunteer and in both cases these visits were appreciated, especially by the lady whose volunteer regularly took her out for a walk. Interestingly, six more people from this small sample would have liked contact with a volunteer. On the other hand, almost half the sample said a volunteer was not needed.

The meals on wheels service and, in one sense help received from neighbours, if they were not being paid, were services on a 'volunteer' basis. However, these can be considered as contacts over which elderly people have some selection and choice and not as volunteers being specially selected for them. Contents of interviews indicated there were probably potentially important roles for volunteers which might be acceptable to elderly people if they were discussed and planned within the context of a comprehensive care programme.

Home help

Detailed information on home help cover has been given in chapter 10. We simply note here that according to our sampling criteria, all sixty nine of the elderly people interviewed were to be provided with home help on their discharge from hospital. In fact, at two weeks, the home help service which had provided two visits to him, was cancelled by one man.

Three people who had had operations for cataracts required daily eyedrops. These were put in by a home help, who visited twice daily for this propose. No special training or instruction had been given to these home helps about administering eye drops. However, they did not feel they required this as they had had to do this task for their own family at sometime in the past.

Day hospital and day care

The elderly people were questioned directly about day care and the grids indicated that only two people went to day hospital once or twice each week, and another lady was taken to an old people's club. There was need for more day hospital care, with transport, in the views of some elderly people, their carers and the interviewers.

Most services and informal care were provided to people in their homes. This predominance of the domiciliary-base of services and informal care networks has to be viewed in the context of the alacrity with which many people made friendships with other patients in hospital, and that many people were disabled, housebound and lonely. Perhaps there is a need for community care planners to reconsider the balance between services provided in the home and services provided in groups in day centres, resource centres or other places. On the other hand, some elderly people may be reluctant to accept day care (see for example, Kirkman, 1984) and they may dislike 'traditional' day care facilities. Perhaps the development of resource centres will lead to different attitudes towards day care. Further study seems to be required here.

Chiropody

Table 11.2 shows that one in three of the sample said they were visited by a chiropodist. Six (11%) said they would like chiropody but were not currently receiving it. It will be recalled that four fifths of the people in the sample were either unable or had difficulty in cutting their own toe-nails. In view of the obvious immobility and instability of most of these people on their discharge from hospital, it may be wondered whether the condition of their feet had received adequate attention.

Health visitor

Only five people said they were in contact with a health visitor (Table 11.2). Two more people would have liked contact. It is uncertain whether some of those who were interviewed were accurately distinguishing health visiting from other types of service.

Social Worker

Half the referrals had been made to organisers by hospital social workers. We do not know if and how these referrals involved personal contact between hospital social workers and the elderly people in the sample.

However, two weeks after discharge eleven people said they were in contact with a social worker (Table 11.2) and three more would have liked such contact. We have earlier described that over half of admissions had been unplanned; almost half the sample had experienced surgery; a third of those who were able to reply to the question had been in hospital for over one month; and a third were probably depressed. Therefore, even in this small sample it seemed there were a variety of situations which may have exacerbated social problems and made referral to a social worker appropriate.

General practitioner

Two thirds of the sample said they were in contact with their general practitioner (Table 11.2) and most were satisfied with the amount of contact they had. Only six people (9% of the sample) wanted more contact with their general practitioner.

Mobile library

One fifth of the sample were visited by a mobile library and three more people would have liked such visits.

Although a mobile library served residents in the local authorities in which people were interviewed, several people in our sample did not apparently know of the existence of this service. Several were very interested. Most people had described their vision as either 'poor' or fair and so access to large print books was important. It seemed that reading was at least as important an activity for many as watching television. The interest of elderly people in reading had also been expressed during a previous study (Neill *et al.*, 1988).

Services and type of referral

We have looked at whether individual services were being received by the elderly people. Overall, as Table 11.2 shows, there was no difference between referral to mainstream services and referral to schemes in the receipt of certain weekly services. An expected association between receipt of community nursing and referral to hospital discharge schemes was not borne out by this feasibility study. This could be because the schemes that we studied were social services schemes, not health service schemes.

However, Table 11.2 does suggest that, counting the number of four weekly services received by the sample, apart from home help, there were small differences between schemes and mainstream cases. Mainstream cases were associated with a higher number of services.

Differences for some of the 'less than weekly' services were slightly more marked. For example, people referred to mainstream services were more likely to be in contact with a social worker. Furthermore, whereas half the sample, overall, were in contact with more than one of these services, only a third of people referred to schemes compared to two thirds of those referred to mainstream services had such contact.

When all the types of service are added, the differences between type of referral and number of services are compounded. These differences, which should be treated with caution given the small sample, are intriguing and deserve testing. For example, chapter 10 shows that home help provision from mainstream services is less intense, on discharge, than schemes provision. Thus the greater contribution from less frequent services associated with mainstream referrals appears as a kind of compensation.

It is unclear whether organisational factors or the characteristics of the elderly people themselves, or the actions of other people in this extended network are at play.

'Cover' and care by networks

The interaction of statutory health and social services, with surveillance and help from relatives and neighbours, was crucial in the daily care of the people in the sample and especially so in the case of those who were very disabled and housebound. In terms of 'cover' the three most important components were relatives, friends and neighbours and social services, especially home help. But, however intensively a home help service may be provided, there are many hours of the day and night when statutory helpers are not present. The components of these people's care networks, informal carers and statutory services together formed a greater or lesser degree of 'cover' during each week. It seemed important to try to see what cover was being provided and what was being done for the elderly people by whom.

Cover by relatives

'Cover' meant whether a person was visited at all during a 24 hour period. Such visits ranged from somebody who 'popped-in' for 10 minutes to somebody who stayed with the elderly person for several hours.

The fact that relatives lived reasonably near to an elderly person did not mean that they visited them. Although most people had relatives who lived within visiting distance, care from relatives as reflected in the grids completed by our interviewers, was provided to only two fifths of the people in this sample.

For example, of the five people who had daughters living next door, or 'over the road' only two received regular visits from a daughter. The reasons for lack of regular visits from relatives were not explored. In one or two cases visits were infrequent or unpredictable. For others, the ages, states of health and other responsibilities of these relatives were important, as were the quality of relationships within extended families and the attitudes of the elderly people themselves.

Equal proportions of men and women received cover from relatives who either lived locally or further away. These regular visits appeared to vary according to the age of the elderly person. Half of those aged eighty years, or older, received cover from relatives, compared to just over a quarter of the people aged between seventy five and seventy nine years.

As well as the ten people who were either living with relatives or who were visited by a daughter living nearby, twelve elderly people were visited at least three times each week by their sons or daughters. Daughters-in-law and sons-in-law were part of this care network. Eight of these twelve people were visited daily, including weekends, although this involved their relatives making journeys of half an hour or more by car or public transport. A further four elderly people were visited regularly at weekends by relatives.

In summary, therefore, the major seven days per week responsibility for providing cover for a quarter of this group of elderly people was assumed by their closest relatives.

Cover by friends and neighbours

Friends and neighbours formed part of the care networks for nearly half the people in the sample. They seemed slightly more likely to be in contact with women than with men. Where elderly people did have friends or neighbours as part of their care network, nearly half were visited daily. These friends and neighbours were mentioned as a fundamental part of the daily care network of over one in three of the elderly people. They popped in daily to one quarter of the sample, and were a major source of contact with the outside world.

Cover by health and social services

Overview of the usual care network during an 'average' week for each person showed that social services provided sole cover on between one to seven days each week for 48% of the sample. Health services provided sole cover on at least one day for very few people.

It would seem that one third of the sample had no contact with either a statutory service provider or an informal carer on at least one day of each week. One man was apparently completely isolated since he had cancelled his home help. The elderly people with the greatest number of self-care difficulties were more likely than the less disabled to have at least one day of the week when somebody from social services was their only visitor.

Interestingly, people referred to mainstream services, who were receiving a larger number of services than those referred to discharge schemes, were more likely also to have informal carers in their networks. Reasons for this can only be conjecture. It could be that mainstream organisers, most of whom worked in 'patches', were more familiar with local networks and better at involving informal carers. Alternatively, schemes' organisers might be biasing eligibility for their service towards people who lack relatives or friends.

To some extent organisers in discharge schemes and mainstream services tried to plan 'cover'. This was difficult especially as each component appeared to operate its own set of priorities and biases, some of which have been described. The 'cover' of home help also had to be reactive to other services, such as community nursing. Presumably such planning will be the province of care managers in the future.

Care by relatives

The physical conditions of this sample of people two weeks after their discharge from hospital has been described. Two thirds experienced difficulty with at least seven self-care tasks. Most still felt unwell and were in some degree of pain and a third were possibly depressed. These difficulties, at this point in time, were continuous from day to day.

There was variety in the support given by relatives. Some relatives only 'popped-in' for 10 minutes 'to make sure she is alright'. Presumably, this meant ensuring that the elderly person was still alive or had not fallen. Other relatives were providing full 24 hour nursing care. The burden on such carers will be discussed later.

Specific questions were not asked of the elderly people, but it seemed most relatives assisted with some aspects of personal care although there was little mention of relatives cutting an elderly person's toe-nails. Relatives also helped with 'business and money' matters. When asked, four out of five elderly people said they had somebody they could confide in and in most cases they named a relative.

Like neighbours and home helps, relatives also were willing to help with an elderly person's shopping. This was one of the tasks which people in the sample most wanted to do for themselves.

Some relatives regularly took the elderly person by car back to their own homes for a meal. Usually this happened during the weekend and often on Sunday. One elderly couple were taken out to the local fish and chip shop every Saturday night. Impressions were that these regular simple outings were of crucial importance in maintaining an 'unwell' person's buoyancy and motivation.

Care by friends and neighbours

Friends who were interviewed did not identify themselves as 'carers' but as 'friends'. That the roles of neighbours and friends formed an important part of the care network of one in three of these elderly people is certain, but we lack information about precisely what they were prepared to do, what the elderly people would permit, whether payment was involved and what taboos existed in these relationships. Elderly people may or may not have shared aspects of personal care, or discussion of finances with these friends depending upon the nature of the relationship.

Friends and neighbours varied in what they did for these elderly people. Some neighbours were being paid, but unfortunately questions about payment to neighbours were not asked systematically. These elderly people were often reluctant for their neighbours to be interviewed—implying that their neighbours were 'nosy' or that they did not 'like their business discussed with the neighbours'. More commonly, relationships with neighbours and friends were rooted in the many years in which most of these elderly people had lived in the same place. A reciprocal relationship was evident in some. For example, the husbands of a young mother and an elderly person who were neighbours had both died at similar times. These two widows had helped and confided in each other despite the difference in their ages.

Minimal help from a neighbour could be crucial, for example:

A recently bereaved 90 year old man lived alone, was very independent, lonely, deaf and with poor vision. His hip had dislocated at least seven times in recent years and when this occurred he was in great pain and completely immobile. He had no telephone, a home help once each week and no friends or relatives to visit. Putting a light in his window to his neighbour was his only signal that he needed help. He paid his neighbour for this service and for bringing him lunch on a Sunday.

Apart from issues about gaps in service provision to this man, the fact remains that his arrangement with his neighbour was enabling him to remain in his home. It was an arrangement he had made himself and therefore accepted.

In general, neighbours and local friends performed two tasks. They provided crucial on-the-spot surveillance and they did shopping. This confirms the findings of other studies (Levin *et al.*, 1989) in which it was found that neighbours were usually unwilling to empty commodes or to help an elderly person with their personal care. However, there were some neighbours and friends who did these tasks.

Social isolation

Only one person was completely isolated in that he had no relatives or friends at all. Furthermore, this person cancelled the home help service within a short time after its provision and remained without services or social contacts. He had a history of mental illness which made him suspicious of personal contacts. His physical disability was severe, his need for help was acute but he had no social worker. This was a situation which clearly needed referral to a social worker who was experienced in assisting people with mental health problems. However, because he was elderly, this person had become the responsibility solely of the home help service.

Around one in five of the people in the sample were very socially isolated. Five people had no local relatives or friends, five did not know if their relatives or friends were living because they were no longer in contact with them, and others had friends or relatives with whom there was only sporadic contact. As has been described, one third of this sample of people were aged between 85–97 years. Their peers were also elderly and if they had 'children' these would be nearing retirement.

Elderly people, at least those in this sample, were often distressed at feeling of little use, under stimulated intellectually, housebound and lonely. Inappropriate demands for friendship were then placed on visitors to the home such as home helps, and home helps themselves could feel emotionally liable for providing surveillance to those who were isolated and living at risk. Such surveillance is probably more effective if given by people living nearby. This vicious circle of social deprivation in relation to those who were housebound after their discharge is a crucial factor in understanding the care networks of these people, in evaluating its effectiveness and in considering implications for future community care services.

Summary in the context of community care

Most elderly people in the sample had lived in their present accommodation for many years and had strong local roots. Although nearly all had at least one relative or friend who lived locally, they had surprisingly few local contacts.

The care and cover provided by local contacts was patchy. On the one hand, having relatives living nearby did not necessarily mean they were in contact with these elderly people. On the other hand, some locally based relatives, neighbours and friends gave regular and extensive help.

Statutory services, especially home help and meals on wheels, were key components in the care networks of these vulnerable elderly people.

Shortfalls in statutory services were especially evident in care from chiropodists and bath aides. Most people in the sample did not receive these services, although two thirds could not cut their own toenails and one third could not have an unaided bath. There was no evidence that most were helped with these tasks by their home helps, relatives or friends.

The interactions of services with help from relatives, friends and neighbours provided extensive cover and care for a minority of people after their discharge from hospital. For most, gaps in the timing and type of care remained.

Chapter 12

Outcomes—the organisational context

One of the aims of this study was to explore the outcomes at three months of two types of home care, those provided by mainstream services and those by hospital discharge schemes. Because of the small numbers in the sub-groups we did not expect statistically significant findings. We sought rather to document various outcomes of these types of service provision and to suggest ways in which outcome measures might be further developed. This task proved to be even more difficult than we anticipated. There are several reasons for this.

Firstly, despite past and current legislation it is still difficult to identify with precision the basic acceptable standards for the components and mix of community care. What, precisely, are the standards below which community care services should not drop and why?

Secondly, evaluation is related to time. This research examines a situation at two points separated by a brief period of three months. Decisions about 'effectiveness' three months after discharge may not encompass prevention of further difficulty in the medium-term. Although 'prevention' may be difficult or impossible to prove, common sense and experience show that 'evaluation' which is too inflexibly short-term may involve ignoring some situations where deterioration could almost certainly be arrested or delayed.

Thirdly, to evaluate the effectiveness of particular aspects of services over time, there is a need to compare like with like so that client prognosis becomes a crucial factor. This has implications for any future research design.

The organisational backgrounds of hospital discharge schemes and mainstream home help services

Before comparing the outcomes of people referred either to schemes or to mainstream services, it is appropriate to discuss the main differences in those two ways of organising community care for people discharged from hospital, as revealed through the researcher's informal discussions.

The hospital discharge schemes in authorities A, B and C each had a small team of specially appointed home helps responsible to only one organiser. As these teams were small (nine or ten people) they each met regularly as a group, learnt from each other and were closely supervised by their scheme's organiser. They became skilled and knowledgeable about helping within situations of illness and had the status of working in a 'special' scheme. They were therefore confident to use their initiatives and to be pro-active in their work. They had to react well to 'crisis' following the hospitalisation of frail elderly people but had the satisfaction of being able to provide help immediately after a person had been discharged from hospital. They were 'freed' to suggest a more intensive or different type of service where appropriate. However, these home helps were required to work towards time-limited goals and to accept distress and frustration if the time-limits of their care were inappropriately and inflexibly applied to individual people.

Unlike organisers in schemes, mainstream organisers worked in groups, at least in the four authorities in which this research took place, and more often had responsibility for a large number of home helps. This was partly because mainstream home helps tended to be employed on a part-time basis and partly because, despite patch organisation, some covered wide geographical areas, especially in the rural parts of authorities A and C. Mainstream organisers were developing ways of dividing their home helps into small groups for supervision, training and support. Some organisers were also evolving in-service training programmes for the whole group which might consist of twenty to thirty home helps, who were responsible to a group of organisers who worked in the same social services office. Hospital discharge schemes organisers were also developing training programmes and most had regular weekly meetings with their smaller groups of home helps.

Despite such efforts mainstream organisers had to cope with inertia about change. Their home helps did not have the stimulus and freedom of being in a 'special' scheme and they were required to operate their authority's policies fairly inflexibly (for example on charging clients or on giving lower priority to those people who were 'only' referred for help with domestic tasks). When an existing elderly client was admitted to hospital, their 'old' home help tended to pick up on discharge where she had left off on admission and the case might not be reviewed. Whereas some elderly people appreciated this continued contact, others faced new situations arising from their recent illness and needed more energetic re-appraisal than was always available. Home helps who had established a routine of care with an elderly person might not find it easy to take a new look at an old situation unless they were impelled to do so by their organiser.

The volume of work coming into mainstream home help organisers was compounded by the needs of their existing caseloads. Their service was the 'end of the line'. Unlike organisers of hospital discharge schemes they were unable to refer on their existing cases.

As we have described earlier, little notice of referral was given to organisers of schemes, or of mainstream services, but they were expected to be able to provide a service immediately or quickly. Yet both types of organisers had to distribute care to clients within the constraints of an 'allocated' number of home help hours. These hours represented the amount of money the authority was prepared to pay for home help provision to the population for whom the organiser was responsible. A needs-led assessment might influence what a home help did, but a resource-led provision determined how much time could be given to these tasks, the times of day during which help was provided and, to some extent who was eligible for care at all. Opposing forces of needs and resources are familiar conflicts of interests but they are nevertheless facts of life and it is important to consider the outcomes for people discharged from hospital within the over-riding constraints of the total help available.

Furthermore, any new 'scheme' for service provision may uncover demand from a 'new' population of potential clients. Such constraints may limit the enthusiasm of organisers to develop new areas of work. For example, it was not in the interests of organisers of hospital discharge schemes to liaise too well with hospital personnel so that the volume of incoming referrals outstripped the resources available. Similarly, it was understandable that some mainstream organisers were ambivalent about the 'new' work which was being revealed by hospital discharge schemes, when mainstream resources were already thinly stretched. Others were relieved when the cases of people discharged home from hospital quicker and therefore less recovered were being dealt with by another organiser in a discharge scheme.

Mainstream organisers suspected that the work of the hospital discharge scheme organiser in authority C had resulted in more referrals from hospitals to mainstream services. Because this organiser had no team of home helps attached to her she was unable to provide patients with immediate care on discharge and so give mainstream service organisers some relief from precipitous referrals. However, she was often able to foster a comprehensive pre-discharge assessment, to negotiate a good discharge process with hospital personnel and to provide patients with information about the range of care available. The good professional links which this organiser established with many colleagues in the mainstream services in her authority might have arisen more from her experience and personality than from the system itself.

The work of this organiser indicates that if, at discharge, separation of assessment and service provision arises from implementation of the NHS and Community Care Act there could be problems if there is not an open acknowledgement, at assessment, of the terms in which 'effective' service is to be evaluated. These terms should include a clear statement of the current compromise between needs and resources in mainstream services and the variations in criteria for eligibility and priority which exist in autonomous social service 'patch' offices.

The 'outcomes' of referrals made to the hospital discharge scheme organiser in authority C were considered under 'mainstream' referrals and not under referrals made to schemes. This is because all home help services to people referred to the hospital discharge scheme organiser in authority C were provided by mainstream home helps.

Chapter 13

Outcomes—for the elderly people

This chapter describes our methods of measuring outcome, in terms of improvement and deterioration in the elderly people and changes in provision. Firstly, however, we outline the outcomes for the sixty nine elderly people whose experiences have been described in earlier chapters.

The outcome sample

Sixty two people were interviewed both two and twelve weeks after their discharge from hospital. During this period, service from home helps attached to the hospital discharge schemes in authorities A, B and D had ceased and people who required continued care had been transferred to mainstream home help services. As mentioned in chapter 12, referrals to scheme C were all included in mainstream referrals, as home help care was, in fact, provided by the mainstream service.

By the time of the second interview, relatives who had rallied to give care when an elderly person was first discharged from hospital had returned to their own homes and they and the elderly people in the sample had re-established their 'normal' routines as far as possible.

Seven of the sample of sixty nine people were not interviewed on a second occasion. Two people had died, three people were admitted to a nursing home or residential care, one was readmitted to hospital and one refused to be interviewed again. All these cases had been referred to mainstream home help service when they were discharged from hospital.

Interviews with the remaining sixty two people were analysed. In this chapter we first present the context of overall improvement or deterioration as reported by interviewers and confirmed by the researcher. Then we concentrate on four aspects of change. These are changes in:

- physical ability and health as reported by the elderly people themselves;
- the mood and morale of elderly people;
- the amount of home help provision;
- the tasks of home helps.

Examples are given of good and bad repercussions of change, and some of the apparent consequences of hospital discharge schemes and mainstream provision.

Information in this chapter relates only to the sixty two people interviewed at both points in time.

Methods of measuring 'outcome'

Outcome was measured in two ways. First, interviewers completed a precoded evaluation schedule on each case, after the six interviews had been completed. Interviewers were asked to give an overview of whether the elderly person's situation had improved, deteriorated or remained the same. Their opinions were compared with precoded data from other schedules.

The contents of interviews were explored in detail by the researcher. The criteria on which interviewers had based their opinions were assessed within the context of the whole sample. The interviewers' ratings were found to be logical and acceptable.

Secondly, precoded data, derived from similar questions which were asked at both interviews, were compared. Changes in the amount of home help provision were then examined with respect to the self care abilities of the elderly people.

Improvement and deterioration: interviewers' ratings

The people in this sample were old and some had been very ill during hospitalisation. 'Improvement' did not necessarily mean an improvement in their health, for this could not always be expected. Neither did 'deterioration' necessarily mean a progression of illness. 'Improvement', in our terms, meant that an elderly person was able to contain and manage any residual disability without apparent unnecessary stress or suffering in the context of the care networks which existed. 'Deterioration' reflected the fact that the struggle with self care and lower motivation were seemingly interactive. There were many influences on the recovery and rehabilitation of this group of very elderly and disabled people.

In overall terms of their mobility, self care ability, morale and self-confidence during the three months after their discharge from hospital, there was evidence of some improvement in one half of these 62 people. One fifth had remained relatively unchanged although, in a sense, maintenance of a level of independence in people of this age could be considered as 'progress' in preventing their deterioration. Just under a third had deteriorated.

Numbers were small, but there were indications that more intensive home help immediately after discharge from hospital influenced better outcomes three months later. More of the people referred initially to hospital discharge schemes had improved during the three months following their discharge and fewer had deteriorated. Nearly half of those referred on discharge to mainstream services deteriorated during this period compared to a quarter of those who had been referred to hospital discharge schemes.

Changes in self care abilities of elderly people

Comparison of the Guttman ratings two and twelve weeks after discharge, as in Table 13.1, shows that the proportion of people whose disabilities could be described as slight or moderate, or

Table 13.1
Guttman Rating of Disability Two and Twelve Weeks After Discharge (N=62)

Guttman rating of disability two weeks after discharge	Guttman rating of disability twelve weeks after discharge				
	None/slight moderate	Severe	Very severe	Total	
	N	N	N	N	%
None/slight/moderate	7	–	–	7	11
Severe	8	5	4	17	27
Very severe	3	8	27	38	61
Total N	18	13	31	62	
%	29	21	50		100

Table 13.2
Self Care Tasks: Changes in Elderly People's * Reported Abilities Two and Twelve Weeks After Discharge (N=62)

Tasks		Comparison of abilities reported two and twelve weeks after discharge			
		No change: no difficulty at either interview	*Change at 12 weeks improved*: less/no difficulty	*deteriorated*: more difficulty/ cannot do	*No change*: difficulty or cannot do unaided at both interviews
Shop	%	7	8	8	76
Cut toe-nails	%	8	10	10	71
Walk down road	%	10	20	8	62
Prepare meals	%	27	13	10	48
Climb stairs	%	15	18	8	58
Bath/shower/ all-over wash	%	28	12	8	52
Dress/undress	%	45	11	11	32
Put on shoes	%	48	13	5	32
Get in/out of bed	%	53	15	2	29
Get round house	%	47	15	7	31
Wash/shave	%	52	10	8	21
Stand	%	48	27	5	18
Comb hair	%	66	8	8	16
Eat/drink	%	79	5	10	7
Make cup of tea	%	68	13	13	5

* These comparisons relate to the 62 people who were interviewed on both occasions. For a few tasks, 1 or 2 records were missing. These have been excluded from percentages. Percentages may add to less than 100 due to rounding.

who were not disabled at all, had more than doubled. However, one half of the sample remained very severely disabled.

More detailed comparison of changes in separate self care tasks, as in Table 13.2, shows that there was little change in most self-care abilities of this sample of people. In relation to most self-care tasks, abilities were either unchanged or there were similar proportions of people who had improved or deteriorated. The exceptions were in relation to tasks involving mobility, where most improvement had occurred in the three months following discharge from hospital. During this period a quarter of the sample had improved their ability to stand and one fifth were now more able to walk down the road and to climb stairs. On the other hand, three quarters of the sample could still not do their own shopping and three fifths still could not walk down the road unaided.

Pain

Two fifths of the sample described experiencing severe pain when they were interviewed two weeks after discharge and this proportion was similar at their second interview. Although nine of these people rated their pain as less severe, five others described more severe pain than they had experienced when they first came out of hospital.

Mood and morale

Despite their disabilities and pain, people in the sample were uncomplaining about how they felt after their hospitalisation. When replies from the first and second interviews are compared, there was little change in elderly people's statements about how they felt. Half said they felt fairly well or 'so so' at both interviews. Around one fifth felt 'not well' or ill. Also there was neither a change in the depression they revealed through the morale score nor in their expressed feelings of loneliness and being a 'burden' on their carers.

This general finding of 'no change' in mood and morale raises three difficulties. Firstly, it masks, albeit for small numbers of people, clear improvement or deterioration across many variables. Secondly, there is a need to relate such small changes to other outcome measures. Thirdly, there is a need to identify whether it is the same individuals who are consistently showing improvement or deterioration across a number of variables.

Examination of the content of interviews indicated that elusive factors of mood, morale and motivation were probably very important in influencing recovery after hospitalisation. For this reason, replies to questions which had been used to assess morale and depression were explored in more detail.

Loneliness

It will be recalled that 'loneliness' and 'feeling a burden on carers' were both related to the score indicating possible depression. In response to the question *'Do you find yourself feeling lonely?'*, Table

13.3 shows that, overall, the proportion of people experiencing loneliness was unchanged.

Table 13.3
Expressed
Loneliness Two
and Twelve Weeks
After Discharge
(N=62)

	(62)*
	%
Did not feel lonely at either interview	26
Felt lonely at first interview—not at second	21
Did not feel lonely at first interview—did at second	18
Felt lonely at time of both interviews	35

* Includes 1 case for which information was missing and excluded from percentages.

Feeling a burden

Feeling that their care was experienced as a 'burden' by others was also related to the score indicating depression. As shown in Table 13.4, there was little change, between interviews, in the proportion of people who felt they were a burden on others.

Table 13.4
Whether Elderly
People Felt They
Were 'a Burden'
Two and Twelve
Weeks After
Discharge (N=62)

	(62)*
	%
Did not feel a burden at either interview	50
Felt a burden at first interview—not at second	10
Did not feel a burden at first interview—did at second	12
Felt a burden at time of both interviews	28

* Includes 2 cases for which information was missing and excluded from percentages.

In response to questions which related to experiences of 'inner ease' such as 'feeling worried' or 'unhappy in general' or 'feeling anxious about the future', around one third of the sample said that they 'had felt worried about things' during the previous month. A third said they had often felt 'sad, unhappy or weepy'.

Although a half of the sample expressed confidence about their futures at both the first and second interviews, one in three of the sample were unsure about their futures three months after discharge and said that either they were unsure, didn't care, felt frightened, worried or hopeless.

Changes in the
amount of home
help provision:
hospital discharge
schemes and
mainstream
services

All except three of the people who had been referred to a hospital discharge scheme continued to receive some degree of home help provision from mainstream services after the defined period of help from the scheme had elapsed. Referral to mainstream home help services of people who had previously received more intensive help from hospital discharge schemes could present problems to mainstream organisers. Whereas they had been relieved of the need to provide a quick and intensive service during the 'crisis' of discharge, they were now required to manage the transition of people from one type of service to another.

Organisers of hospital discharge schemes had an allocated number of home help hours with which to provide their service. Although the work loads of their home helps could be organised more flexibly than in mainstream services, the overall budget was set. Hospital discharge schemes had to respond immediately to people referred at the time of their discharge from hospital. Schemes organisers therefore had to adhere to the length of time for which intensive help from the scheme was available so that the capacity of the scheme to respond to incoming work was preserved. Passing on the care of some elderly people could be a difficult experience for schemes organisers and home helps. Although their contact with the people they helped was relatively brief, it was obvious that close relationships were often formed. A scheme home help may have shared an elderly person's adjustment to discharge home from hospital and fostered their increasing independence and confidence.

Mainstream organisers, like schemes organisers, had an allocated number of home help hours per week which they had to divide between people requiring the service. These allocations were inflexible and the provision was often tight. Mainstream organisers were therefore continually reviewing and rationing their service and were always aware that if they gave extra help to one person, they were inevitably removing it from another. Issues about how to provide an intensive service to a few people and a more thinly spread service for many, and how these groups should be defined, were an intrinsic part of the work of mainstream organisers. Such dilemmas were reflected in the transition from schemes to mainstream services.

Discontinued home help services

Home help had been completely discontinued to seven of the sixty two people in the sample. Three of these people had been referred to a hospital discharge scheme and four to mainstream services on their discharge. Five of these seven people had improved and two had deteriorated, according to the interviewers' evaluations, by the time they were interviewed on the second occasion.

Decreased home help hours

On average, each person in the follow up sample received 4.2 hours of home help per week two weeks after discharge. This had been reduced to 3.2 hours by the time of the second interview twelve weeks after discharge. By this time there had been a reduction in the number of home help hours allocated to half the people in the sample. As Table 13.5 shows, the sharpest reduction was in the number of people who had received between 5—14 hours of home help per week immediately after their discharge.

Despite these overall reductions, there were ten people who still had between five to fourteen hours per week home help, three months after discharge.

**Table 13.5
Hours of Home Help Provision Two and Twelve Weeks After Discharge from Hospital (N=62)**

Hours per week two weeks after discharge	Hours per week twelve weeks after discharge				Total	
	Home help ceased	Under 2	2–4.5	5–14	N	%
Under 2	6	9	1	–	16	29
2–4.5	1	8	10	–	19	34
5–14	–	2	9	10	21	37
Total N	7	19	20	10	*56	
%	12	34	36	18		100

* Excluding six cases for which information was incomplete.

As people referred to hospital discharge schemes generally received a higher level of home help provision when they were discharged from hospital, proportionately more were 'levelled down' when they were transferred to mainstream services. Thus, two thirds (64%) of the people who had been helped initially by a hospital discharge scheme had their home help hours reduced compared with two fifths (41%) of those who had been referred after discharge to a mainstream home help service.

Maintained home help hours

One quarter of the people interviewed were receiving the same number of hours of home help three months after their discharge as they had when they first came home. This included one third of those who had been referred to mainstream services on discharge and one sixth of those referred to hospital discharge schemes. When interviewed twelve weeks after discharge, according to the interviewers' evaluations, around one half of both groups had improved and a half had either deteriorated or their conditions remained the same.

Increased home help hours

Home help hours had been increased for eight people but the increase in the number of hours was very small. These eight people only received an extra four hours home help between them. Most of these eight people had deteriorated since their discharge and the increase in home help had been in response to this.

Change in the number of days home helps visited

As well as reducing the number of home help hours deployed to most people in the sample, the number of days on which a home help visited had also been reduced. As Table 13.6 shows, three months after discharge, one third of the 'outcome' sample were receiving home help on one day each week and two fifths on between two to four days weekly. The average home help hours per day received by most of these two groups of people was just over one hour per day.

Only a quarter of the sample received home help on between five to seven days per week. This group received, on average, slightly less than two hours of help per day.

**Table 13.6
Elderly People
Twelve Weeks
After Discharge:
Total Home Help
Hours and Number
of Days per week
Visited (N=62)**

Number of days per week home help visited	Total home help hours per week [N=160.3]	Elderly people receiving service (50)*
	%	%
1	14	34
2–4	36	42
5–7	50	24

* Excludes 7 people no longer receiving home help and 5 cases where information was incomplete.

The net reduction in home help hours for the whole sample

When interviewed two weeks after discharge, the 62 people who were interviewed two and twelve weeks after discharge were 'using' a total of 244.5 home help hours between them. Twelve weeks after discharge this total had been reduced to 160.3 home help hours. Therefore, during the three months after discharge there had been a net reduction of 84.2 home help hours or a third of the home help hours originally deployed.

There were differences between schemes. In schemes A and B, compared to scheme D, there were higher proportions of people who had reduced or discontinued home help and higher proportions of people who had improved. However, it will be recalled that the people selected for help from schemes A and B were generally less disabled than those referred to scheme D.

As mentioned earlier, only a quarter of the sample received home help on five or more days per week at follow up. As can also be seen in Table 13.6, a disproportionately larger share of home help hours was deployed to this small group. Although they received, on average, less than two hours of help per day, the repercussions on mainstream home help resources of maintaining even this minimal level of provision to this minority of 'heavy' users was that half the total home help hours were being deployed to a quarter of the sample, twelve weeks after their discharge from hospital.

The tasks of home helps

Although their hours had been reduced, the tasks of home helps remained similar. Three months after this sample of people were discharged from hospital, home helps were mainly helping with housework and shopping and seldom with personal care. However, most (90%) elderly people thought home helps did tasks which were appropriate and necessary.

Exploration of the content of interviews indicated that a minority of elderly people who had difficulty with tasks, such as getting in and out of bed or dressing themselves, would have welcomed assistance. The times at which home helps were provided caused difficulty for some people. *'They are not allowed to start work before 9.00am'*.

Increased charges for mainstream home help, compared with schemes, had also presented problems to some people who had been transferred to a mainstream service and had been reassessed to pay a higher charge for their home help. Some felt they could only afford a limited time for help with essential tasks. In one authority, people who were receiving an attendance allowance were automatically assessed to pay the maximum charge for their home help. In another authority, there was a policy of telling elderly people who were receiving an attendance allowance that if they required help at weekends they would have to employ help privately and pay for this out of their allowance.

A fifth of the people in the sample at the first interview and a third at the second thought 'the home help service could be better'. In most cases this comment was related to the wish for more home help time or for more frequent visits, but some people described the effects of gaps in provision especially during the early mornings and at weekends. However, four fifths of people at the first interview and two thirds at the second interview thought they were getting enough home help.

Disability and number of hours of home help

Although all except eight of the people in the sample experienced a reduction in home help, it was clear that the most disabled people experienced the sharpest effects of any reduction in the number of home help hours and in the number of days in each week on which home helps visited. Although mainstream organisers were obviously attempting to target services to the most disabled, such targeting was less possible than it had been for schemes' organisers.

Whether degrees of disability or self-care difficulty are described by using the Guttman score, as in Table 13.7, or by the eighteen self care tasks, the proportionate reduction in hours of home help to the small group of the most severely disabled people is apparent.

Table 13.7
Provision of Home Help in Relation to Disability: Change in Disability (Guttman Score) between Two and Twelve Weeks after Discharge from Hospital (N=62)

Disability twelve weeks after discharge

	Better			Same/worse		
	Home help hours per week			Home help hours per week		
	(N)	Initial Mean	Difference Mean	(N)	Initial Mean	Difference Mean
Elderly person's Guttman Score two weeks after discharge						
None or some disability	(0)	–	–	(7)	1.7	–0.7
Severe disability	(8)	2.4	–0.7	(9)	3.7	–0.9
Very severe disability	(11)	4.7	–2.2	(27)	5.4	–1.5

* Includes seven elderly people whose home help had been discontinued by their second interview twelve weeks after discharge.

Table 13.7 shows that people who were very severely disabled when they were discharged from hospital but whose self care ability improved during the twelve weeks following their discharge had their home help hours reduced by an average of 2.2 hours per week. People who were severely disabled at discharge but deteriorated to a degree of very severe disability also experienced a reduction of 0.9 hours per week. Those who remained very severely disabled throughout this period had an average reduction of 1.5 hours per week.

Changes in provision: repercussions, 'solutions' and unresolved issues.

Reduction in home help hours was not, in itself, directly related to whether or not improvement or deterioration had occurred. However, the positive effects of intensive help from a hospital discharge scheme were evident. Twelve weeks after discharge from hospital, two fifths of those who had initially been helped by a scheme and who had subsequently had their home help stopped or reduced, had improved, compared with only one in six of those who had been referred from hospital to mainstream services. Thus, two thirds of those who had improved despite a decrease in home help hours, had initially been helped by a hospital discharge scheme. This suggests that intensive help following discharge and good preparation for a decrease in home help service may have enabled improvement to be maintained.

Some people had recovered from their illness or injury. For example:

A lady in her late 80's who had been very ill with an acute infection and in hospital for six weeks was now able to drive her car and resume an almost 'normal' routine. She had been very immobile on discharge and the home help she received not only aided her rehabilitation but reassured her about the quality of care she could expect if she became ill in the future.

On the other hand, there were also examples of deterioration which coincided with the reduction in service. Home help was stopped for an independent and well organised lady who deteriorated after she had *initially* recovered well from an acute infection. Apparently her abilities had been over-estimated and service ceased. When interviewed she was said to be:

'deteriorated, exhausted and depressed. Home help has stopped. Clothes grubby, grease on table and dirty crockery everywhere. Quite different from the neat and confident person she was at the first interview.'

The issue in this case is not whether or not home help should have been discontinued but the need to review the effects of such decisions so that such sharp deterioration might be averted.

The questions raised by these examples are ethical as well as practical. Is it better to have had an intensive service for a short time and have it removed, or is it better never to have experienced the more intensive service which is required and so avoid the distress of imposed change and loss of home help?

It will be recalled that at the time of their discharge from hospital, there was little overall difference in this sample in the degrees of disability of people referred to hospital discharge schemes or to mainstream services. Discharge schemes provided an intensive period of help for two to six weeks, but people whose complete rehabilitation during this time might be expected were not being selected for this special help. The fact that most of those who were initially referred to schemes had to be referred on to mainstream service made the process and quality of transition an important factor in avoiding their unnecessary deterioration.

Selection

A discharge scheme in Northern Ireland (DHSS SSI, 1988) illustrated one way of attempting to avoid the problems of transition. Only elderly people where there was an expectation of recovery and rehabilitation within a few weeks of discharge were selected as eligible for special help from the scheme. It cannot be known whether this group of people might have recovered anyway, albeit at a slower pace, without special help after their discharge. Such selection also raises issues about further discrimination against very disabled people who require such intensive help but on a longer term basis.

Overlap and shared care

This research was not designed to explore in detail the process of transition from a scheme to a mainstream home help service.

Informal conversations with organisers revealed that, in special circumstances, there was some flexibility in the length of time for which intensive help from a scheme was provided, but this was limited by the pressures of new referrals on the scheme. In authorities A and B home helps from the scheme and mainstream service sometimes shared 'cover' of an elderly person. This involved extra effort by these home helps to establish congruent goals and methods with the elderly person and each other. Numbers were too small to evaluate this way of managing transfer, but the researcher's impressions were that such procedures could ease the transition for the elderly person and soften the change for the scheme organiser and home help. It was also interesting that mainstream home helps who had experienced this shared role were said to have learnt from the skill and experience which the scheme home help had acquired. The success of this system clearly depended upon the commitment and team work of the organisers involved, so that the risk of home helps being in competition or conflict over the same elderly person could be avoided. Such a system also depends on some 'give' in the resources of mainstream services.

Information, forward planning and review

Elderly people referred to a scheme were given information at referral about the length of time for which the scheme operated. It was obviously essential that each elderly person knew this. However, interviewers found that some of these people were already worried two weeks after their discharge about how they would manage when help from the scheme ended. Those who had had a home help previously did not know whether they would get their 'old' mainstream home help back again. Neither did they know how much home help time they would be allocated. It cannot be known whether this anxiety inhibited their recovery, but it is reasonable to assume that confidence about the future is an important component of motivation towards achieving maximum independence.

During interviews these elderly people did not convey confidence that the amount of home help available to them would be much influenced by their degrees of disability. Crucially, they were associating potential reduction in their home help with economic factors which were outside their control: *"Rumour has it there are going to be less home helps"*.. The roles of care managers as envisaged in the NHS and Community Care Act will, if adequately resourced, ensure that changes in the amount of a service, such as home help, are firmly linked to the conditions of individuals. In this way reduction in home help might be perceived as a part of the triumph of those who recover. Reduction in home help for the severely disabled and for those who deteriorate will, hopefully, not take place.

Severely disabled people who needed continuing care

Around a third of the sample required long-term help and about a half of these had not had a home help before their hospitalisation. This meant that mainstream home help services were already 'trawling in' a new population which had been identified by the presence of a hospital discharge scheme. Whether or not schemes exist, the numbers of very severely disabled people requiring care in the community after their discharge from hospital will inevitably increase. In this sample, these people were housebound, sometimes lacked reliable contacts with relatives and friends, and their daily lives were often enervating struggles with self-care difficulties. Lack of help with self-care at the times it was needed, feelings of depression and apprehension about the future, coupled with the pervasive effects of being housebound were more than adequate explanations for their deterioration and low morale. This is illustrated by the following case study.

> *An eighty seven year old lady spent a month in hospital after falling and fracturing an ankle. She lived alone but was visited regularly by two sons and elderly friends and neighbours. Her accommodation was, she said, suitable for her despite the damp, the outside WC and the steps down to her kitchen which she could not manage. She had poor vision due to cataracts, and pain from arthritis which she said she 'had learnt to live with'. This lady walked with a stooped gait, slowly and with a zimmer frame. She could not stand for long and had difficulty getting in and out of bed and combing her hair due to her extensive arthritis.*

> *A scheme home help had started the day after her discharge and came for one hour on each week day to do the housework, shopping and provide general encouragement. This was the first time this lady had had a home help.*

> *Two weeks after discharge this elderly lady was cheerful and optimistic. She kept herself occupied with reading, writing letters, watching television and doing jig-saws, but complained that the weekends were boring. She was waiting for the aids and adaptations which had been ordered.*

> *Twelve weeks after her discharge this lady's mainstream home help had been reduced to two hours on one day per week. Her mobility was much worse and the interviewer said 'she looks much older, she seemed depressed and suppressed tears during the interview. Last time she was cheerful and vivacious'.*

> *Her sons now visited on alternate days and not every day as before. Help from elderly friends and neighbours was also less regular. The general practitioner did not visit. Some aids and adaptations had been provided, others were still awaited.*

> *This lady complained more of her severe pain during this second interview and said she was in pain even if people touched her. She was frightened of walking and felt lonely. The interviewer said*

'After she was so optimistic about getting better her arthritis got worse and became more painful. She has become very depressed and has lost her optimism and will to improve. This change has coincided with a reduction in her home help'.

This lady was typical of others who deteriorated. In this case, home help had been reduced because it was the policy within the local authority not to provide mainstream home help to people who only required help with housework tasks. Although such tasks were what the home help actually did for this person, the regular support and encouragement the home help also provided might have been a crucial influence on this elderly lady's motivation to struggle on with a very painful and disabling condition. This person valued her independent life-style, yet it seemed likely that inadequate care in the community might eventually drive her into residential care or hospital.

Unresolved questions and issues

Other examples, at least as grave as this, could be provided even from this small sample of elderly people. This minority of very disabled people represent a silent minority whose situations raise questions about whether they are in receipt of community care or community neglect. In general, they were uncomplaining partly because they were touchingly grateful for the small amount of help they did receive and feared losing it and partly because they were in touch with few people with sufficient 'clout' to whom they could complain.

A necessary policy of providing the minimal amount of home help to such 'long-term cases' had repercussions which were apparent three months after discharge. Feelings of personal insult and humiliation were particularly evident in the minority of people in the sample who needed continuing care because of their extreme disability but where home help was sharply reduced. Most of these people were living in conditions which raised serious questions about the minimum level and standards of services which should be accepted. For example:

–   Is it permissible for a commode to remain unemptied in an occupied room for two or three days over a weekend? This would not be allowed in a prison.

–   When a commode has to be placed in a room where a person is eating and sleeping, should the provision of a chemical commode be mandatory?

–   If adequate community care for this 'heavy' end group is to be provided, should home help be available to cover early morning and evening times and weekends if necessary?

–   Could mainstream home help services be resourced, trained and encouraged to be more pro-active in their attempts to assist with self care tasks for severely disabled people who are unlikely to recover their abilities?

- Can the delivery of essential aids and adaptations be guaranteed prior to or synchronised with discharge from hospital? If not, should such delay be considered a sufficient cause for delaying discharge?

- Are modern methods of pain control being fully utilised in the care of elderly people who say they are in severe pain?

- Should more energetic effort be made to assist housebound disabled people to go outside the confines of their own homes if they wish?

Summary in the context of community care

Despite improvement in the conditions of some elderly people during the twelve weeks after their discharge from hospital, nearly 90% continued to require home help.

There had been a reduction in home help hours to most people who continued to have this service. Those who had been referred initially to hospital discharge schemes had the sharpest average reduction in hours because they had been given more hours initially after their discharge from hospital. However the condition of a higher proportion of this group had improved since their hospitalisation.

Over half the sample remained housebound and severely disabled twelve weeks after their discharge from hospital. In the researchers' views, they required more intensive and frequent care with a wider range of tasks than current levels of mainstream home help provision could provide, given the constraints on resources.

Two fifths of the elderly people who were interviewed twelve weeks after discharge were very severely disabled indeed. In relation to their disabilities they were receiving a minimal level of home help service. Two weeks after discharge from hospital they were only receiving, on average, 5.4 hours of home help each week. When interviewed again twelve weeks after discharge the hours of home help deployed to them had been cut by an average of one and a half hours per week.

The resources of mainstream home help services were stretched and referrals from discharge schemes had a further knock-on stressful effect on these resources. Although mainstream home help hours were targeted to the most disabled people in the sample, there was a higher average reduction in hours to the people who were most severely disabled and who needed the service most.

Despite this reduction, a half of the total mainstream home help hours deployed to this sample twelve weeks after discharge were being given to a quarter of the elderly people in the sample.

When directly asked, elderly people expressed satisfaction with the home help service. In spite of this, mainstream organisers, constrained by their budgets, were aware and concerned about shortfalls in care to the minority of very severely disabled clients who were in the sample.

In our views, meeting the needs of disabled, housebound old people requires continued attention from planners and service providers. The often sad situations of those who have had their home help provision reduced or stopped, in the face of a poor care network, for reasons other than an acknowledged improvement in their physical, emotional and social condition, are likely to increase numerically as more very severely disabled people are cared for in the community.

Interviews with this sample of elderly people indicated there was urgent need for basic practical standards of service delivery to be established and for resources to be made available to meet these standards. In particular, unemptied commodes, the non-provision of aids and adaptations and the isolation of the housebound need attention.

Chapter 14

Outcomes—for the carers

A 'carer' was defined as 'the relative or friend who gave the elderly person most help on a day to day basis'. Twenty eight carers were interviewed two weeks after the discharge from hospital of the elderly person for whom they cared and twenty seven carers were again interviewed ten weeks later. There were several reasons for the fact that it only proved possible to interview carers for less than half the people in the sample. Firstly, interviewers were inconsistent in the persistence with which they sought and recorded permissions from the elderly people to interview their closest carer. The researcher's secondment to a Social Services Inspectorate project had meant that supervision in the field was curtailed. The low carer sample was, in part, a casualty. Secondly, there was genuine reluctance on the part of elderly people as described below.

Identity of carers

Eight people in the sample did not have any close carer who could be identified. The closest carer of a further six people was somebody employed by one of the services, such as a home help, sheltered housing warden or day care manager. In most cases the elderly people had known these 'professional' carers for several years.

Twenty people had a carer who was a neighbour or friend. Our sample of elderly people were generally reluctant for their neighbour or friend to be interviewed. The reasons given where usually because *'they did not like their affairs discussed with the neighbours'* or because, friends who cared were identified by elderly people as 'friends' rather than as carers. Conversations with the friends who were interviewed revealed that they also perceived themselves in this way and any help or support they gave to the elderly person stemmed from friendship and not because they perceived themselves as carers. Where elderly people had given permission only reluctantly for their carers to be contacted, subsequent interviews with these carers confirmed that the instincts of these elderly people could be well-founded. Some neighbours and friends seemed alarmed and surprised to find themselves identified as a person's principal 'carer', for this awareness carried an implication of responsibility which was not always welcomed.

Thirty six elderly people had carers who were relatives. Reluctance about interviewing relatives seemed to stem from anxiety that any further demands on their 'carers' might tip the fine balance of care on which they depended.

Seven of the eight people who lived with a 'carer' lived with a spouse or sibling who was also elderly; one person lived with her son. Another person in the sample usually cared for her disabled sister and so she was both a 'patient' and a carer. She was therefore interviewed as a 'patient' two weeks after her discharge from hospital. Three months after her discharge she had again become a 'carer' and was therefore also asked questions which related to the tasks and stresses of caring, as well as questions about her own experiences of hospitalisation.

Tasks performed by carers

Although numbers were small, it was clear that only a minority of these carers, between one fifth and a quarter, helped elderly people with personal care tasks such as getting in and out of bed, putting on their shoes, getting dressed, washing themselves, having a bath or cutting their toe-nails. Two fifths of the carers did light housework. Most carers (70%) did some of an elderly person's shopping. As mentioned earlier, shopping was a task also done by home helps but was one activity which most elderly people would have liked to have done for themselves. Unlike home helps, around a half of the carers helped an elderly person to prepare meals and a quarter of the carers helped an elderly person to walk down the road and regularly supported them up and down stairs or steps. One third of the twenty seven carers regularly gave help with at least one self-care difficulty.

There was an overall congruence between the replies of elderly people and their carers about the sensory abilities of people in the sample, whether they were in pain and whether they had difficulties with sleep. However, carers tended to rate an elderly person's pain as less severe than the elderly person had reported.

Stress on carers

Three quarters of this small group of carers described some degree of personal stress arising from their caring tasks and a third said this stress was severe. For two thirds of carers there was also some physical strain and one fifth said this was severe. The proportions of carers experiencing such personal and physical stresses were similar two and twelve weeks after the elderly person had been

143

discharged from hospital. For half the carers the burden of other responsibilities interacted with these other types of stress to make helping the elderly person difficult.

Example of personal stress compounded by other responsibilities

> *When her very disabled mother was discharged from hospital an only daughter travelled from Hampshire to London to visit three days each week. This daughter was a single parent who had two school-aged children, one of whom was physically disabled. The physical and financial demands of this routine were bad enough, but it was the personal stress of dividing her care between her mother and her own disabled daughter which gave this caregiving daughter the most stress. As long as her mother received several visits per week from a discharge scheme home help the caregiving daughter felt reassured that, if she was unable to visit, her mother would have a safety net of care. When the scheme ended and home help was reduced, this daughter's own stress and exhaustion increased. Three months after her mother's discharge from hospital the daughter was also ill and unable to visit. The possibilities of the caregiving daughter's own hospitalisation and the admission to residential care of her disabled child were being considered.*

Example of physical stress

Carers who were themselves elderly could lack the physical strength to lift and support another person who was weak since their recent hospitalisation. For example:

> *A husband had cared for his wife for years, despite being disabled himself and having a leg amputated some years previously. This wife's recent hospitalisation for acute infection had been coupled with a worsening of her existing arthritis and her night time 'frequency'. Two weeks after his wife's discharge home from hospital her husband was coping well, with intensive help from a hospital discharge scheme worker. He had plans to take his wife on holiday and to renew his own social contacts and activities, which had lapsed during his wife's hospitalisation. Ten weeks later his home help had been decreased. The physical strain of interrupted nights and supporting his wife around the home was apparent from this husband's appearance as well as from what he said. He complained of pain in the stump of his own amputated leg and he had cancelled plans for a holiday for them both because he felt they could not cope in a strange environment. The help he gave his wife with her personal care had now become onerous.*

The interviewer commented:

> 'He looks exhausted. The light and vitality seems to have gone out of his eyes. He seems to be much older and frailer himself, and he is depressed about the future for himself and his wife'.

It is probable that this husband would have found the stress of caring too great whether or not the home help hours had been decreased. The fact that these hours had been cut when this husband felt he was coping well and was feeling more optimistic about a difficult situation penalised him for his efforts. The amount of physical and emotional strain this man experienced had increased to some extent, but his capacity to withstand it had deteriorated considerably.

Example of personal stress associated with finance and loss of leisure

> *A divorced son lived with and cared for his very disabled mother who had become more immobile since her hospitalisation. He was in full-time employment and went to work on his motor bike. His passion for motorcycles was reflected in his sole leisure activity of motorcycle scrambling during weekends and all his personal friendships were associated with this. Because her son was in full-time employment this mother was assessed to pay the full cost for her home help. Although more home help hours per week were offered, the mother and son could not afford more than one hour per day. This meant the son came home during his lunch hour to ensure his mother had a meal and received any help she required. He came straight home from work in the evenings and had to give up his weekend motorcycling activities because home help was unavailable at weekends and there were no relatives or friends prepared to give his mother the personal care she required.*

The interviewer commented:

> *'This situation is a time-bomb. This son is coping at the moment but how long he can keep it up is an open question. He has no life or social activity of his own at the moment. There is danger that he will start to resent his mother because of the personal cost of his caring'.*

Quality of relationship between carer and elderly person

Two fifths (41%) of carers interviewed thought that their relationship with the elderly person for whom they cared had changed in recent years. All except two carers said their feelings towards the elderly person were usually positive or 'ordinary' and they experienced a similar positive reaction towards them from the elderly person. However, half the carers said they thought the elderly person felt they were a 'burden' to others. This had been confirmed by statements of the elderly people themselves. Changed relationships had had to accommodate a new aspect of inequality which arose from one person giving care which was received by the other.

Carers' own health

Nearly half (46%) of the carers said their physical health was good or 'average' but one third reported that it was only fairly good or that it was bad. There was little change in the physical health of most carers between the first and second interviews, two and twelve weeks after the elderly person's discharge from hospital. The health of three carers had improved and three had deteriorated.

There were more slight repercussions of caring on the mental health of carers. At the first interview over two thirds (70%) reported they often (35%) or sometimes (35%) felt anxious or depressed. Slightly fewer (50%) felt like this ten weeks later.

'Breaks' from caring

Stress on carers was usually unremitting. Most of the carers said they had not had a 'break' from the responsibility of caring since the elderly person had been discharged from hospital. In most cases this was because there was nobody available to assume this role, even temporarily. Although there could be several extended family members who lived locally, it was usually one person who assumed the major caregiving responsibility. This has been found in other research also (Levin and Moriarty, 1990; Levin *et al.*, (1989); Qureshi and Walker, 1989; Twigg *et al.*, 1990; Williams and Fitton, 1991).

Carers were asked to whom they turned for understanding and emotional support. All except two of the nineteen carers for whom this question was relevant named their spouse or another relative. Two carers said they had nobody to whom they could turn. The importance of carers receiving relief is the subject of much current research. If they are to continue caring without undue stress it is essential to enable carers to continue their social contacts and leisure activities.

Carers' views of home help services

Three out of four carers had met the home help who was visiting and they appreciated their personal contributions. However, half the carers at both interviews said that they thought the home help service could be improved. One quarter of the carers at the first interview and two fifths at the second said that the elderly person for whom they cared needed more home help than he or she was receiving. Similar proportions listed tasks which they would like home helps to do in this extra time. There was a suspicion amongst the small group of carers who were interviewed, and especially those who were neighbours or friends, that the more they did for the elderly person, the more their help would be taken for granted by service providers. In the words of one neighbour:

'The more you do, the more they will let you get on with it'.

Who is 'the patient?'

As described, most carers were themselves elderly. In some cases, twelve weeks after 'the patient' had been discharged from hospital it was difficult to distinguish whether it was the designated 'patient' or their carer who was most in need of help.

Organisers did their best to assess the needs of the elderly people within the context of the physical strength and emotional

146

resilience of their carers. Although they understood the problems of carers, demands on home help resources to meet situations of more acute need meant that they were often unable to provide help for the sake of the carer rather than for the benefit of the designated 'patient'.

In the short-term, reliance on informal carers could help reduce demands on services, such as home help. In the longer-term, the examples of this small group of carers indicated that with some there was a real risk of producing two 'patients' rather than one.

Summary in the context of community care

Less than half the elderly people in the sample gave permission for their closest carer to be interviewed. Reasons for refusal included already feeling they were a 'burden' on their carer and apprehension about placing an extra demand on them.

Relatives and friends who made special efforts and arrangements to give care during the 'crisis' of hospitalisation and discharge often could not maintain this level of care on a longer term basis. Three months after these elderly people had been discharged from hospital their care from relatives and friends had returned to 'normal' levels. Consultation with relatives and friends who provided special care after discharge might have clarified the stressful repercussions of their efforts. Earlier help to carers who were apparently 'coping' may have enabled some to have continued for longer, as they apparently wished.

Elderly people were aware of and apprehensive about stress on the carers on whom they depended. This nexus of anxiety was clearly affecting the confidence and morale of some people in the sample.

Most of the small groups of carers who were interviewed described personal or physical stresses. For some these were severe. Some carers were as old as the elderly people who were interviewed. Other carers, such as the children of these elderly people, were around retirement age.

Problems relating to their physical health were reported by half the carers and over two thirds said they felt anxious or depressed. The physical and emotional well being of carers had shown little change in the three months following the elderly person's discharge from hospital.

The importance of a joint assessment of an elderly person's abilities, in the context of the health and ability of his or her carer, cannot be over emphasised.

Chapter 15

Conclusion: some implications for policy and practice of selected findings

Introduction

The guidelines for good practice, which are given in the Department of Health booklet *Discharge of Patients from Hospital*, influenced our thinking during the preparation of this report. The completion of the report coincided with the Department of Health's publication of three guidance booklets on care management and assessment, in preparation for full implementation of the NHS and Community Care Act. These are: *Care Management and Assessment, Managers' Guide* (SSI, 1991a); *Care Management and Assessment, Practitioners' Guide* (SSI, 1991b); and *Care Management and Assessment, Summary of Practice Guidance* (SSI, 1991c). These documents represent a guide for social services managers and practitioners for the future and are the context in which we make some recommendations arising from this research. However, good official guidance can only be translated into more effective practice if the relevant services are resourced to a level which enables such guidance to be implemented. There is increasing concern that adequate resources for community care may not be forthcoming (Harding, 1992).

The scope of this research

The feasibility study described in this report was a small initial study into a large subject. The constraints of our sample, which include the small sample size, the small number of schemes sampled and the selective eligibility criteria, limit the potential for generalising the findings. The sample was intended to provide a basis for an initial exploration of the impact of services received on discharge from hospital and the effects over time of these. In this feasibility study, it was more important to identify the issues and their possible implications than to estimate the frequency of particular issues or problems. This the study has done.

The discharge of elderly people from hospital has long been recognised as an important interface between health and social services, which is highly sensitive to any change in policy or practice from either side. The hospital discharge schemes on which our research was based were set up in response to changes in the hospital sector. However, these schemes were all financed and run by social service departments. Hospital discharge schemes financed by voluntary organisations, health authorities or jointly financed might have different characteristics and different outcomes for patients. For example, health authority schemes might result in more input from community health personnel, such as community nurses. Furthermore, as the national telephone survey described in chapter 2 shows, no two hospital discharge schemes were identical. To overcome this problem, the study draws out some of the specific characteristics of the services which may be common to them.

The scope of this conclusion

Despite the constraints of this research we are able to draw together some issues and to present possible implications which arise in the provision of services on discharge from hospital, and to make a limited set of recommendations for further consideration. These are considered under three broad headings:

    A   Pre-discharge planning and hospital discharge schemes.
    B   The discharge process.
    C   Care in the community.

Under each heading we: state our assumptions about the realities in health and social services at the present time and in the near future; refer to the context of guidance from the Department of Health; present key findings; draw out policy implications and give recommendations for good practice.

A. Pre-discharge planning and hospital discharge schemes

Assumptions

The tempo of admissions to and discharges from hospitals is unlikely to decrease. In-patient stays may become shorter. Increase in day surgery and treatments may mean very old people will be discharged even quicker and therefore sicker because they will be in a less recovered state. Consequently, there will be increased pressures on social service resources. Issues about which authority should be financially responsible for care during these periods of recovery at home are not the remit of this research, but if left unresolved, and a history of poor collaboration continues, negative knock-on effects on the quality of service delivery can be expected.

With so many elderly people being discharged from hospital, for most, the ideal of a considered, more leisurely medico/social assessment is likely to conflict with the need for quick di‍
and speedy and adequate provision of services.

Department of Health guidance

' ... *under no circumstances should the patient be put at risk or used as a pawn, for example, through coerced discharge home. . .'* (SSI, 1991a: para. 4.53).

'Hospitals and local authorities should agree discharge procedures that are designed to cause as little delay as possible. . .' (SSI, 1991a: para. 4.56).

Findings

1. Our research, supported by other studies, suggests that *hospital discharge schemes offered a more timely and integrated service* to elderly people leaving hospital and scored higher on a count of 'good discharge procedures.'

2. Some *advantages* of schemes:
    (i)   they provide a quick and high quality service to patients for a brief period after discharge;
    (ii) the organiser can have personal contact with patient and carers before and after discharge;
    (iii) through regular personal contact with ward staff the organiser can obtain better information, sometimes act as an advocate for the patient and re-negotiate discharge dates when appropriate.

3. Some *disadvantages* of schemes:
    (i)   there can be a knock-on effect on mainstream home help services;
    (ii) help is time-limited;
    (iii) they can become too popular and silted-up;
    (iv) they can increase inequity of provision;
    (v)   they can be expensive, given limited social services resources.

Policy implications

1. *Hospital discharge schemes which provide high quality assessment and adequate service provision, on discharge from hospital, should be encouraged.* Such schemes are focussed on the needs of patients and carers and are not only concerned with the quick clearance of hospital beds.

2. A discharge scheme organiser may provide elderly people with a *personal link during their transition from hospital to home and assessment both in the context of a hospital ward before discharge and in their own homes afterwards.* If implementation of the NHS and Community Care Act means that assessment at discharge and the provision of services are conducted by different people, discharges might be delayed, assessment less holistic and there might be fewer opportunities for evolving better discharge procedures with hospital staff.

3. A discharge scheme needs to be *planned as part of an overall policy* for and with mainstream home care and not as a special 'project' which is financially unstable. Thus, it should be experienced by mainstream services as an additional resource and not as a liability.

4. Schemes need to be part of a policy of dynamic, targeted and planned change in the *relationships between local hospital, social services and primary and community health care.*

Recommendations for practice

1. The aim of *enhancing the effectiveness of schemes* should be pursued by ensuring that schemes organisers and their home helps:
    (i)   are equipped to respond quickly and appropriately to discharge. They all need to be casual car users, able to be in immediate contact through bleeps and employed on the understanding that they may have to work unsocial hours on seven days per week;
    (ii) are responsible for discharges from a restricted number of hospitals to enable them to be in regular personal contact with ward staff;
    (iii) have a team responsibility. Two or more home helps may share 'cover' for individual patients. Senior home help(s) may share some administrative responsibility with the organiser;
    (iv) work in tandem with mainstream service home helps when possible and appropriate;
    (v)   do not become isolated from mainstream social services.

2. The *roles of scheme home helps should be extended* to enable them to:
    (i)   meet a ward nurse with those patients who are especially disabled or in pain so that the most comfortable and effective ways of caring for them are fully understood;
    (ii) if necessary, act as an escort home for those patients who have no relatives or friends able to do this;
    (iii) if necessary, prepare the homes of those patients who have no relatives or friends able to do this.

3. Steps should be taken to *meet the needs of scheme organisers and their home helps* for:
    (i)   *membership* of peer groups in mainstream community services, especially if the scheme is based in a hospital;
    (ii) *training*. Although they become experienced and skilled at helping within situations of illness, they need further information about certain illnesses and disabilities, the side effects of medication, reactions to loss and available aids and adaptations;

(iii) *confidential consultation and supervision* to enable them to respond appropriately to distress in clients and their families and to cope with their own reactions. This applies especially to situations of terminal illness. This type of supervision may not be most appropriately given by line managers;

(iv) *information* about changes in policy and practice relating to their service and help with implementing change, especially if this means refusing service to clients;

(v) *regular review* of the progress of their scheme in relation to targets of improved liaison with the hospital(s). Organisers may need line managers to share responsibility for negotiating with professional groups.

B. The discharge process

Assumptions

The increased tempo of admissions and discharges to and from hospital, together with the current shortage of nurses and the use of agency staff, is likely to undermine the quality of information circulated. In time, the humanitarian goals of user participation, as outlined in the National Health Service and Community Care Act, may be jeopardised.

Department of Health guidance

'...discharge plans must be agreed with patients and with all individuals and agencies that are expected to contribute to their implementation. Before agreeing to the plan, users should have the likely cost explained to them ...' (SSI 1991a: para. 4.52).

Findings

In our sample:
(i) two fifths had relatives who rallied to provide special help and turned discharge into a family celebration, but *half were not in this fortunate position;*

(ii) most hospital admissions had been *unplanned;*

(iii) most people *lived alone* or with another elderly person;

(iv) one fifth were *seldom visited* in hospital by relatives or friends;

(v) the *cumulative repercussions* of the above indicators included patients returning home to decaying food and unheated rooms;

(vi) delays in *transport* were common. This meant that the day of discharge could be a disappointing and exhausting experience. It was not unusual for a patient to wait on the ward from early morning until evening for an ambulance for the journey home;

(vii) hospital car service drivers did not usually see patients indoors, possibly because they were volunteers, might themselves be elderly and were uninsured for this task. Some patients *could not negotiate the steps to their front door* without considerable help;

(viii) essential aids, such as commodes, were usually provided before, or soon after discharge, but patients waited several weeks or even months for other *aids and adaptations*.

Policy implications

(i) A policy of planning for discharge should *start at admission to hospital* or as soon as possible afterwards.

(ii) A policy of *screening* in order to identify the most vulnerable and isolated patients should be considered. The systematic use of the three indicators of *unplanned admission* and *living alone* and *being without regular visitors in hospital* could be tried.

(iii) Policy relating to provision of *transport* needs to be reviewed. It should include ensuring that unattended or frail patients are safely and comfortably installed in their homes. Transport policy should also include arrangements for elderly or unfit carers who take elderly people home in their own cars to be given assistance to support an immobile patient indoors, if necessary.

(iv) The respective *roles of qualified ambulance crews* and the volunteer drivers of the *hospital car service* should be reviewed in relation to the needs of disabled elderly people who need to be supported as well as transported on their discharge.

(v) An enquiry is urgently needed to explore the reasons for delays in the supply of *aids and adaptations*. The ambiguities, gaps and overlaps between health and social service provisions need to be identified and removed.

(vi) A policy of *publicising the roles* and responsibilities of home helps should be considered. *Routine circulation of clear information* to all those who refer people to the home help service would help to make their expectations more realistic.

(vii) *Criteria defining what constitutes a good discharge* should be established and made available to those responsible for drawing up the relevant contracts of care.

(viii) As outlined in the National Health Service and Community Care Act, patients and carers should be provided with *information* about the services which are available, and their associated charges, so that they may participate in plans for their care after discharge.

Recommendations for practice

(i) A *'Going Home Folder'* might be given to elderly patients when they are admitted to hospital. In this folder, professionals, patients and carers could record facts relevant to discharge. This might ensure that the patient obtains essential information before discharge, and gains the confidence to ask about the repercussions of illness and the purpose of medication. It might also help professionals to recognise the most vulnerable people and take early action in preparation for their discharge.

(ii) Organisers, or those responsible for assessment, should always be *invited to trial home visits.*

(iii) Transportation must be taken more seriously and not left to chance. Patients or their relatives should *be told about the possibility of delay* when the hospital is responsible for organising transport.

(iv) Home helps should be given simple guidelines for assessment to help them to understand the process of discharge and recovery, so that they can *participate in ongoing assessment* and review.

C. Care in the community

Assumptions

Amongst people aged seventy five years or more, there will always be a minority who need long-term intensive care. Most people will prefer to remain in their own homes. Organisers of mainstream home help services will continue to face dilemmas about providing a thinly stretched service to many people or an intensive service to a few. However, we must assume that most elderly people will continue to depend for their support, not primarily on health and social services, but on their personal care networks. These may or may not be supported by an ethos of care within their local communities.

Department of Health guidance

'Where the assessment is concerned with the maintenance of a person at home, the assessment should take place in that setting..' (SSI, 1991b: para. 3.13).

'. . . services . . . are designed to ensure that old, infirm or handicapped people can, if they wish, live in the mainstream of society with dignity and respect. . .' (DH, 1991).

Findings

In our sample:

(i) almost all had lived in their *present accommodation for many years,* wished to remain there, and had roots in the local community;

154

(ii) almost all were *strongly motivated* towards recovery and increased independence;

(iii) on discharge, most of the elderly people *felt ill*, were severely *disabled*, and *housebound*. Two fifths were in *pain* and a third were possibly *depressed*. Some elderly people had a very poor quality of life;

(iv) although most people did not usually receive help with personal self-care tasks they expressed *satisfaction* with home help with their *housework*;

(v) at discharge, the *predicted level of home help* required was accurate in less than a third of cases;

(vi) transition from a hospital discharge scheme to a mainstream home help service meant, for most people, a reduction in home help provision, a *financial reassessment* and sometimes a *new scale of charges* and a *change of home help*;

(vii) *care networks* were comparatively small;

(viii) there was a *shortfall in chiropody and bath aide* services.

Policy implications for assessment procedures

(i) There should be a policy of *early reassessment* after discharge to identify whether the provision of home help is *adequate and correctly targeted* to assist rehabilitation.

(ii) A minority of people who are likely to remain very disabled or become increasingly dependent will *require further full assessment*, which may be multi-disciplinary and include assessment of personal care networks. Severely disabled people should be assessed both when they are in hospital and also when they have been discharged into their own homes. This would enable assessment of such elderly people to be conducted within the context of their usual environments, within the context of the ability and commitment of their carers and within the context of potentials and constraints in the care networks in their locality.

(iii) *Planning for long term care* for this small group of very disabled people should not be delayed until help from a hospital discharge scheme ends. For example, doctors should be asked to review the medication of those who describe severe pain. Elderly people who may be depressed should be referred for specialist assessment and help. Being unwillingly housebound for long periods should be regarded and treated as a potential hazard to mental health, motivation and recovery.

(iv) Assessments should routinely *identify shortfalls* in provision, such as *chiropody, bath aides* and the need for specialist advice on *vision and hearing*.

(v) When an elderly person is discharged into the care of another elderly person, there should be an assessment of the health and social care *needs of the household*, couple or group and not just of the designated 'patient'.

(vi) Relatives, friends or neighbours who respond to an elderly person's discharge from hospital by taking an active part in their care should be seen by the assessor, if the elderly person agrees. Their help should *not be taken for granted.*

(vii) There should be regular review assessments to evaluate the *effectiveness* of the services being received.

Policy implications for service provision

(i) The contribution of *home help with housework tasks* to a person's motivation and recovery should be reconsidered. A clean and orderly environment can help to sustain motivation and improve recovery, as well as limit risks.

(ii) Home help organisers, or care managers, should always review and evaluate the progress of people who have had their *home help discontinued or severely cut*, for example, because they become ineligible through 'only' requiring help with housework.

(iii) Guidance on the *basic minimal standards of service* provision which are acceptable could be considered. This might include, for example, the number of hours during which an unemptied commode may remain in an occupied room.

(iv) Where services are restricted, *charging policies* should not prevent home helps from paying short visits of 10–15 minutes to those people known to be at risk.

(v) *Transport facilities* should be reviewed so that disabled people can be offered visits to resource centres for facilities such as chiropody, an assisted bath, assessment for aids for vision and hearing, and enjoyable experiences such as a visit to a hairdresser. This might provide some elderly people with welcome social contact and might also be a more economic way of providing services which are in short supply.

(vi) The legality of charging policies, applied by some authorities but not others, which require elderly people to pay for *care at weekends* from their attendance allowance, should be reviewed and clarified.

(vii) A policy of *active rehabilitation* of those people who require a short period of more integrated and intensive care than is possible in their own homes, could be pursued by extending day and residential rehabilitation facilities staffed by skilled personnel such as physiotherapists and occupational therapists.

Recommendations for practice

(i) A *'Care at Home Folder'* could be offered to each elderly person. This would contain the names, addresses and telephone numbers of service providers. It would be the property of the elderly person and they, their carers or any professional could make notes in it about matters such as a change of home help or holiday dates. This folder would be similar to the community nursing records which are kept in patients' homes.

A minority of our sample of elderly people were clearly going to need long term assistance of an intensity which, possibly, the mainstream home help services were currently not equipped to provide. It is this group who are at the sensitive interface between residential care, readmission to hospital and care in the community. However, our sample indicated that these very disabled people were strongly motivated towards remaining in their own homes. The stresses and conflicts of interest presented by this group are many, and their individual choices are easily eroded. This is a key group as far as the NHS and Community Care Act is concerned, and their experience provides a measure by which the success or failure of the Act may be judged.

Appendix

Thoughts on home helps by elderly people

"The successful ones are a special breed. The set-up is perfect. It was vital to my recovering so rapidly. Extra home help left my friends able to feel uninhibited and to visit me without feeling they *had* to help."

"It's very nice to have someone in the mornings when I'm slow and worried about the future."

"I'm fed up with home helps. She only came once and then had a fortnight's holiday."

"Has hair like a sheep-dog—an enormous mop of hair. Youngish, grey-haired. She's sweet, excellent, awfully nice. Willing to do anything —except brass."

"Comes in and does her job without any fuss or bother to me. Would like her to clean windows and tidy the garden. I'm not sure what they are meant or allowed to do. Wish they could spend more time with me. They are always in a rush and very busy."

"She's a worker. Does the floors lovely. A big made girl. Has a loud mouth. I wouldn't be without her."

"Small, quick, agile, good memory. Comes when they can fit you in. Would be nice if they came when you wanted them."

"We need home helps for "men's work"—odd jobs, repairs, drains."

"Large motherly lady. Full of fun. Does you the world of good."

"One is always in a rush to get away. The others are very good."

"I never ask her to do anything—just let her get on with it. I'd like the kitchen cleaned every week, but home helps do not like moving things—like pulling out the spin dryer. They don't clean in the corners—not like I would do myself. The home help service does not have a very good name—you're lucky if you get a good one."

"Chatty, friendly, willing, caring. Rather tallish. A hefty wench. Has a couple of kids. We are real mates."

"A young man. He's cheerful. Makes a cup of tea if I want it and a sandwich.

"Home helps should be allowed to do more things than they are allowed to do—like moving furniture, emptying the hoover bag. The home helps don't look for work."

"A big girl, but dresses nicely. We have a good laugh. She's got a smashing car."

"I would like a statement of tasks. This one has to be told or she does not do what you need. One week I had no food in the house. You have to put up with their ways, or get into their bad books."

"Elderly, very dressy. Very nice and pleasant to everybody. Takes an interest in me. I feel I can trust her."

"Home help is the most wonderful thing I've discovered in life. Without them it would be pretty grim. They are very helpful. I would find it difficult to do all the things that have to be done. The first time you meet them you tell them and if it's within their range of duties they do it. They can even clean my inside windows. A wonderful organisation."

"Quite a nice person. I let her get on with it. She would just wade in if things piled up. She's cheerful, has lots of initiative."

"Very charming willing lady—happy disposition."

"My special home help was waiting for me when I came home. I'd feel lost without her. I think it's pretty good."

"Would like a little more time for a good clean. We are friends. Rumour has it that there are going to be less home helps."

"Some home helps empty the commode into the sink—that's awful. Others empty it into the garden—that's better."

Thoughts on elderly people by home helps

"She was just bewildered—she needed convalescence but she was just dumped at home. She needed me. She cried when I left."

"I would like an introduction to the client before the first day. If I had not worked in a nursing home, I would need some training in personal care."

"They would like help with little things they have not got the confidence for—silly little things like moving a plant and they don't like to ask. They need someone to re-assure them when they don't have relatives near by."

"It all comes down to money. You pay for what you get. Home helps should be able to do more things and not be restricted."

"It's my job—we have a laugh sometimes. She gets depressed and cries quite a bit and sometimes she gets angry but not with me. I don't take any notice when she shouts at me."

"This case is straightforward but sometimes it's very different. You find out when you get there. The organiser assesses what is needed, but it can all change by the time we get in. I feel we should be able to broaden what we are allowed to do. We need to be a nurse to do these things."

"I would like special training and be able to compare with the quality of work of other home helps. I think it's apathy. They should go into a nursing home for a week to see how things are done. I do lots of work I'm not paid for like taking washing home and ferrying clients around."

"I think our service is really vital. I love my job—think it is important. I've had training for first aid and lifting at the local hospital—I would like to know more about what to do in case of emergency."

"We are not supposed to talk to other home helps about cases."

"As a home help, you are a doctor, nurse, mother and auntie."

"I usually 'read up', but I would like more medical knowledge; how to cope with people who are terminally ill, diabetes etc."

"We need some sort of service to check what they really need. So much is needed. When services are requested it is not accepted coming from a home help—good neighbours appear to get priority. A 'helpline' should be set up for home helps to contact."

"The job has changed over the last 10 years. Now it is more controlled because of the activities of the unions which has made things better for workers, but worse for clients. The future is not attractive. Things are likely to get more and more commercialised and less personal. I would like practical demonstrations on how to cope with disabilities, ideally a day on a pre-discharge ward with the nurses."

"There are different courses to go on. I have been on ten. The discharge team is small, so you can get quick access to the organiser. When working on the Area you feel like one in a million."

"I wish there was more time to 'give attention' i.e. to stop and listen to clients."

"I get worried over leaving food and knowing she might not eat it. Worry over danger with electrical things and her opening the door to strangers. Her confusion totally threw me. I would like to have visited her with the organiser the first time. There was no money to buy client anything. I'd like training about dementia."

"I would like training—more information—more experience—like I went to a lady with double amputation. People with disabilities like that need someone every day. They are anxious about who is coming in when the special scheme is finished."

References

Age Concern Liverpool (1975) *Going Home? The Care of Elderly Patients after Discharge from Hospital. Report on the Continuing Care Project*, Age Concern, Liverpool.

Amos, G.M. (1973) *Care is Rare: A Report on Homecoming for the Elderly Patient*, Age Concern, Liverpool.

Arber, S., Gilbert, G.N. and Evandrou, M. (1988) 'Gender, household composition and receipt of domiciliary services by elderly disabled people', *Journal of Social Policy*, 17, (2), 153–175.

Audit Commission (1985) *Managing Social Services for the Elderly More Effectively*, HMSO, London.

Bird, A.S., MacDonald, A.J.D., Mann. A.H. and Philpott, M.P., (1987) 'Preliminary experience with the Selfcare (D): a self-rating depression questionnaire for use in elderly, non-institutionalized subjects', *International Journal of Geriatric Psychiatry*, 2, 31–38.

Butt, J., Gorbach, P., and Ahmed, B. (1991) *Equally Fair: A Report on Social Services Departments' Development, Implementation and Monitoring of Services for the Black and Minority Ethnic Community*, Race Equality Unit, London.

Caldock, K. and Wenger, G.C. (1988) *Elderly People and the Health and Social Services (Rural North Wales) 1979–1987*, Centre for Social Policy Research and Development, University College of North Wales, Bangor.

Chadwick, R. and Russell, J. (1989) 'Hospital discharge of frail elderly people: social and ethical considerations in the discharge decision-making process', *Ageing and Society*, 9, 277–295.

Challis, D. and Davies, B. (1986) *Case Management in Community Care: An Evaluated Experiment in the Home Care of the Elderly*, Gower, Aldershot.

Connor, A. and Tibbitt, J.E. (1988) *Social Workers and Health Care in Hospitals: A Report from a Research Study*, Central Research Unit for Social Work Services Group, Scottish Office, HMSO, London.

Davies, B. and Challis, D. (1986) *Matching Resources to Needs in Community Care*, Gower, Aldershot.

Department of Health (1989) *Discharge of Patients from Hospital*, DH, London. See also: local authority circular LAC(89)7; and health circular HC(89)5.

Department of Health (1991) *Achieving the Change—Secretary of State's Speech: Progress Review Issues for SSI/RHAs*, DH, London.

Department of Health (1992) *The Patient's Charter*, HMSO, London.

Department of Health and Social Security Social Services Inspectorate (1988) 'Short term support for elderly people discharged from hospital', *PSS in N. Ireland, 36*.

Exton-Smith, A.N. (1977) 'Functional consequences of ageing: clinical manifestations', in Exton-Smith, A.N. and Grimley Evans, J. (eds.) *Care of the Elderly: Meeting the Challenge of Dependency*, Academic Press, London.

Fenton Lewis, A. (1981) 'Fracture of neck of the femur: changing incidence', *British Medical Journal*, 283, 1217–1220.

Gorbach, P. (forthcoming) 'Clarifying the framework' in overview report for the Social Services Inspectorate home help-home care inspection programme, SSI, Department of Health, London.

Grimley Evans, J. (1979) 'Fractured proximal femur in Newcastle upon Tyne', *Age and Ageing*, 8, 16–24.

Harding, T. (1992) *Great Expectations ... and Spending on Social Services*, National Institute for Social Work, London.

Hedley, R. and Norman, A. (1982) *Home Help: Key Issues in Provision*, Centre for Policy on Ageing, London.

Holyoake, T.I. and Semple, P. d'A. (1990) 'Comparison of acceptability by General Practitioners of word processor and conventional discharge letters', *Health Bulletin*, 48, 1, 29–35.

Hunt, A. (1978) *The Elderly at Home*, HMSO, London.

Kirkman, D.R. (1984) *The None-Use of Community Social Services by the Frail Elderly: A Case Study in an Outer London Borough*, M. Phil. thesis, Goldsmith's College, University of London.

Levin, E., Sinclair, I.A.C. and Gorbach, P. (1989) *Families, Services and Confusion in Old Age*, Gower, Aldershot.

Levin, E. and Moriarty, J. (1990) *"Ready to Cope Again": Breaks for the Carers of Confused Elderly People*, Research Unit, National Institute for Social Work, London.

National Corporation for the Care of Old People (1978a) *'Getting Better?': Report 2: the Care of the Elderly Returning Home from Hospital*, Continuing Care Project, NCCOP (now Centre for Policy on Aging), London.

National Corporation for the Care of Old People (1978b) *'Help! I Need Somebody': Report 3: A Study of the Aftercare Needs of Elderly Patients leaving Hospital*, Continuing Care Project, NCCOP, London.

The National Health Service and Community Care Act 1990, HMSO, London.

Neill, J., Sinclair, I.A.C., Gorbach, P. and Williams, J. (1988) *A Need for Care: Elderly Applicants for Local Authority Homes*, Gower, Aldershot.

Office of Population Censuses and Surveys (1983) *Great Britain: Census 1981: Sex, Age and Marital Condition*, HMSO, London.

Office of Population Censuses and Surveys (1984) *Population Projections 1981–2021, Series PP2, no. 12*, HMSO, London.

Office of Population Censuses and Surveys (1987) *General Household Survey 1985*, HMSO, London.

Parker, R.A. (1981) 'Tending and social policy' in Goldberg, E.M. and Hatch, S. (eds.) *A New Look at the Personal Social Services*, Policy Studies Institute, London.

Parker, R. (1990) 'Private residential homes and nursing homes' in Sinclair, I., Parker, R., Leat, D. and Williams, J., *The Kaleidoscope of Care: a Review of Research on Welfare Provision for Elderly People*, HMSO, London.

Prudham, D. and Grimley Evans, J. (1981) 'Factors associated with falls in the elderly: a community study', *Age and Ageing*, 10, 141–46.

Qureshi, H. and Walker, A. (1989) *The Caring Relationship: Elderly People and their Families*, Macmillan, London.

Sinclair, I. (1990) 'Carers: their contribution and quality of life' in Sinclair *et al.*, *The Kaleidoscope of Care* (op. cit.).

Sinclair, I., Crosbie, D., O'Connor, P., Stanforth, L. and Vickery, A. (1988) *Bridging Two Worlds: Social Work and the Elderly Living Alone*, Gower, Aldershot.

Skeet, M. (1970) *Home from Hospital*, Don Mason Florence Nightingale Memorial Committee, London.

Skeet, M. (1985) *Home from Hospital: Providing Continuing Care for Elderly People*, Kings Fund Centre, London.

Social Services Inspectorate (1987) *From Home Help to Home Care: An Analysis of Policy, Resourcing and Service Management*, SSI, Department of Health and Social Security, London.

Social Services Inspectorate (1990) *Inspecting Home Care Services: A Guide to the SSI Method*, HMSO, London.

Social Services Inspectorate and Social Work Services Group (1991a) *Care Management and Assessment: Managers' Guide*, HMSO, London.

Social Services Inspectorate and Social Work Services Group (1991b) *Care Management and Assessment: Practitioners' Guide*, HMSO, London.

Social Services Inspectorate and Social Work Services Group (1991c) *Care Management and Assessment: Summary of Practice Guidance'*, HMSO, London.

Stone, M., Barton, A., Coles, O., Dodds, M. and Smith, J. (1989) 'Supporting frail elderly people at home: comparative study of two domiciliary care services', *Journal of Management in Medicine*, 4, 3, 171–178.

Townsend, J., Piper, M., Frank, A.O., Dyer, S., North, W.R.S. and Meade, T.W. (1988) 'Reduction in hospital readmission stay of elderly patients by a community based hospital discharge scheme: a randomised controlled trial', *British Medical Journal*, 297, (6647), 544–547.

Twigg, J., Atkin, K. and Perring, C. (1990) *Carers and Services: A Review of Research*, HMSO, London.

Victor, C.R. (nd) *A Survey of the Elderly After Discharge from Hospital in Wales: Final Report*, Research Team for the Care of the Elderly, Welsh National School of Medicine, St David's Hospital, Cardiff.

Victor, C.R. and Vetter, N.J. (1985) 'The use of community and rehabilitation services by the elderly 3 and 12 months after discharge from hospital', *International Rehabilitation Medicine*, 7, 2, 56–59.

Walker, J. (1991) 'Living with pain', *Nursing Times*, 87, 43, 28–32.

Williams, E.I. and Fitton, F. (1988) 'Factors affecting early unplanned readmission of elderly patients to hospital', *British Medical Journal*, 297, 784–87.

Williams, E.I. and Fitton, F. (1991) 'Survey of carers of elderly patients discharged from hospital', *British Journal of General Practice*, 41, 105–108.

Williams, J, (1990) 'Elders from black and minority ethnic communities' in Sinclair *et al., (op. cit.).*

Williamson, V. (1985) *Who Really Cares?: A Survey of the Aftercare of Elderly Patients Discharged from Acute Hospital*, Brighton Community Health Council.

Young, E., Wallace, P. and Victor, C. (1991) *Older People at the Interface: A Study of the Provision of Services for Older People within Parkside Health Authority*, Occasional Paper No.10. Helen

Hamlyn Research Unit, Department of General Practice, St Mary's Hospital Medical School, London.

Further reading

Abramson, J.S. (1990) 'Enhancing patient participation: clinical strategies in the discharge planning process', *Social Work in Health Care*, 14, (4), 53–71.

Armitage, S. (1985) 'Discharge referrals—who's responsible?', *Nursing Times*, 20 Feb., 26–28.

Armitage, S.K. (ed.) (1991) *Continuity of Nursing Care*, Scutari Press, London.

Association of Community Health Councils of England and Wales (1986) *Patients' Charter: Guidelines for Good Practice'*, ACHC, London.

Bagley, G. (nd) *'From Hospital to the Community: A Report Examining Discharge Procedures from Hospital and Community Provision for Elderly People*, Research/Development Office (Elderly), Good Hope Hospital, Sutton Coldfield, West Midlands.

Barton, A, Coles, O., Stone, M., Dodds, M. and Smith, J. (1990) 'Home help and home care for the frail elderly: face to face in Darlington', *Research Policy and Planning*, 8,1, 7–13.

Brocklehurst, J.C. (ed.) (1985) *Textbook of Geriatric Medicine and Gerontology, Third Edition*, Churchill Livingstone, London.

Cooper, L. (1991) 'Adult discharge planning and nursing home placement: a study of risk factors for quality assurance', *Australian Clinical Review*, 11, (73), 95–102.

Coulton, C.J., Dunkle, R.E., Chow, J.C., Haug, M. and Vielhaber, D.P. (1988) 'Dimensions of post-hospital care. Decision making: a factor analytic study', *The Gerontologist*, 28, 2, 218–223.

Department of Health (1989) *Caring for People: Community Care in the Next Decade and Beyond*, Cm 849, HMSO, London.

Department of Health (1989) *Working for Patients: The Health Services. Caring for the 1990s*, Cm 555, HMSO, London.

Department of Health and Social Security Social Services Inspectorate (1992) *An Inspection of Social Work in General Hospitals*, Department of Health Social Security Inspectorate, Belfast.

East Anglian Regional Health Authority and Office for Public Management (1990) *Rubber Windmill. Contracting for Health Outcomes: a Report of a Workshop to Explore the Workings of an Internal Market in the Health Service, held in East Anglia—April 1990*, EARHA, Cambridge.

Evans, E., Farnsworth, S. and Howard, M. (1987) *Review of the Special Care (Early Hospital Discharge) Scheme*, Gloucestershire County Council Social Services Department.

Fordyce, I.A. and Hunter, D.J. (1987) 'Rural-urban variations in service provision for elderly people', *Journal of the Royal College of General Practitioners'*, 37, 109–111.

Harding, J. and Modell, M. (1989) 'Elderly people's experiences of discharge from hospital', *Journal of the Royal College of General Practitioners'*, 39, 17–20.

Hopkins, A. and Maxwell, R. (1990) 'Contracts and quality of care', *British Medical Journal*, 300, 919–22.

Howard, D.J. 'Structured discharge letter in a department of geriatric medicine', *Health Trends*, 18, 1, 12–13.

Isaacs, B. and Evers, H. (1984) *Innovations in the Care of the Elderly*, Croom Helm.

Livingstone, G., Hawkins, A., Graham, N., Blizard, B. and Mann, A. (1990) 'The Gospel Oak Study: prevalence rates of dementia, depression, and activity limitation among elderly residents in Inner London', *Psychological Medicine*, 20, 137–146.

Marks, L. (1991) *Hospital Discharge*, a review of the literature for the Audit Commission, London, (unpublished).

Marshall, B. and Levett-Williams, S.A. (1987) 'Liaison between the community and an acute hospital for the elderly', *Health Visitor*, 60, 328–9.

Neill, J. (1989) *Discharge from Hospital of Frail Elderly People: Telephone Survey: Interim Report of Main Findings*, Research Unit, National Institute for Social Work, London, unpublished.

Neill, J. (1989) *Assessing Elderly People for Residential Care: A Practical Guide*, National Institute for Social Work, London.

Perkins, E. (1991) 'Screening elderly people: a review of the literature in the light of the new general practitioner contract', *British Journal of General Practice*, 41, 382–385.

Rao, N. (1991) *From Providing to Enabling: Local Authorities and Community Care Planning*, Joseph Rowntree Foundation, York.

Schorr, A.L. (1992), *The Personal Social Services: An Outside View*, Joseph Rowntree Foundation, York.

Victor, C.R. and Vetter, N.J. (1988) 'Re-arranging the deckchairs on the Titanic: failure of an augmented home help scheme after discharge to reduce the length of stay in hospital', *Archives of Gerontology and Geriatrics*, 7, 83–91.

Young, E., Wallace, P. and Victor, C. (1991) *Older People at the Interface: A Study of the Provision of Services for Older People within Parkside Health Authority*, Occasional Paper No.10. Helen Hamlyn Research Unit, Department of General Practice, St Mary's Hospital Medical School, London.

Young, P. (1988) 'Home-care assistants: a new multifunctional role', *Geriatric Medicine*, 18, 8, 31–34.

THE HEREFORD & WORCESTERSHIRE COLLEGE OF NURSING & MIDWIFERY WORCESTER CENTRE

Printed in the United Kingdom for HMSO
Dd294505 9/92 C15 G531 10170